PENGUIN HANDBOOKS

THE SLIMMER'S COOK BOOK

John Yudkin has been Professor of Nutrition and
Dietetics in the University of London since 1954. Born
in 1910 he proceeded from Christ's College, Cambridge,
to the London Hospital and later did research work in
the Biochemical Laboratory and the Nutritional Laboratory at Cambridge, where he was also Director of
Medical Studies at Christ's College. His degrees include
M.A., M.D. (Cantab.), B.Sc. (Lond.), M.R.C.P., and F.R.I.C.
From 1945 to 1954 he was Professor of Physiology at
Queen Elizabeth College, University of London. He has
published many articles on biochemistry and nutrition
in learned journals.

Gweneth Chappell, who is an M.Sc. (Physiology) and
Ph.D. (Nutrition), graduated at Queen Elizabeth College. After a short period as a social worker for the
L.C.C., she joined the staff of Queen Elizabeth College,
where she has done research work and published papers
on various aspects of foods.

John Yudkin *and* Gweneth M. Chappell

THE SLIMMER'S COOK BOOK

PENGUIN BOOKS

Penguin Books Ltd, Harmondsworth, Middlesex, England
Penguin Books Australia Ltd, Ringwood, Victoria, Australia

—

First published by MacGibbon & Kee 1961
Published in Penguin Handbooks 1963
Reprinted 1965, 1967, 1969, 1970

—

Copyright © John Yudkin and Gweneth M. Chappell, 1961

—

Made and printed in Great Britain
by C. Nicholls & Company Ltd
Set in Linotype Juliana

CONTENTS

PREFACE

THE ideas, recipes, and menus in this book are intended primarily as a guide to those who are following the dietary principles set out in *This Slimming Business*. There, we saw that the best and most effective diet for slimming was also the best and most effective diet for health. It is quite wrong to imagine that, in order to lose excessive weight, you have to eat in such a way that you will feel tired, weak, and miserable. On the contrary, your loss of weight will be achieved on a diet which is likely to be nutritionally better. The chances are that it will make you healthier than you have ever been before. For this reason, the menus and foods here can be shared by every one of the family; you don't have to cook specially for yourself and separately for the family.

Let us recall the principles of this plan of eating, which will both make you slim and keep you healthy. They were, firstly, that you should cut down as much as possible on foods containing carbohydrates (sugar and starch) – foods like sweets, biscuits, bread, cake, and puddings. Secondly, you should eat those foods which will give you all the protein, vitamins, and mineral elements you need. This means that you can eat as much as you like of those foods which contain no sugar or starch – meat, fish, eggs, cheese, butter, cream, margarine. If you do this – if you change to this new and better way of eating – three things will happen. First, you will lose your excessive weight. Secondly, you will not feel hungry. Thirdly, you will reach a level of health which you have forgotten – or never even knew – to be yours.

The recipes and menus are, of course, not exhaustive; we could have filled a book with meat dishes only. What we have tried to do is to select dishes which would be representative: simple homely dishes, as well as elegant party dishes: meals which you can 'knock together' in minutes, as well as ones which will take you quite a long time. The newcomer to the kitchen will find quite adequate instructions, while the expert cook can produce endless variations on some of the themes we give.

We have especially kept three things in mind. The first is that we have given you a wide choice of inexpensive dishes. People believe that dishes which are rich in protein and fat must be expensive. Well, it is true that potatoes, sugar, and bread will fill you more cheaply than best steak, Dover sole, and Stilton cheese. But there are other cuts of meat, other sorts of fish and cheese. And though you *could* fill yourselves with cheaper foods than stewing beef, cod, and Cheddar cheese, you would certainly not be so healthy. Remember too that you will be saving money on the sweets and chocolates, cakes and biscuits.

The second point is to remind you that these slimming principles include sociability. You can stick to your way of eating at the same table as your non-slimming family or guests even at a grand dinner. And no one needs to notice. Don't take a roll. Leave out the rice with your soup. Don't take sugar with your pudding. Many of our recipes therefore will contain something with starch or sugar, but designed in such a way that you can quite easily leave out that part of the course. At the worst, no harm will come to you even if you do occasionally have a small helping of a special party dish which does contain carbohydrate.

The third point we have made is that it is perfectly possible to make box lunches and similar 'take away' snacks without the use of a lot of bread and cake and other carbohydrate-rich foods. So often have we heard people complain that they cannot 'keep to the diet' because they have to take a packed lunch with them. So we have made a special section on 'portable' low-carbohydrate dishes.

We hope that this collection of recipes will show you that foods which make you slim are also foods which make excellent dishes and meals. We believe that your friends will like them as much as yourself. We are sure that you will also be eating in the healthiest possible way.

INTRODUCTION

MANY of you reading this book will be vastly experienced cooks, but some of you may still get tripped up by some of the simpler stumbling-blocks. To help you to avoid these, you will find it useful to read the following few pages.

Baking temperatures

The best of recipes will be a flop – sometimes literally! – if you use the wrong temperatures. Most gas cookers nowadays have a numbered dial (e.g. Regulo). The temperatures (Fahrenheit) for the different numbers should be as follows:

¼=240°	5=380°
½=265°	6=400°
1=290°	7=425°
2=310°	8=445°
3=335°	9=470°
4=355°	

Sometimes, however, the settings for the temperatures are different from these. It is always worth while to check for yourself. It takes a little time, but you can save hours of anxiety – and lots of wasted foods – by taking this trouble. First, get yourself a good thermometer – it's no use checking for the accuracy of your cooker with an inaccurate thermometer. Put the thermometer in the centre of the oven, light the gas, and put the dial at ¼. Allow at least twenty minutes, open the door, and quickly read the temperature and record it. Now move the dial to ½, wait ten minutes, and read the temperature again. Continue until you have checked every number of the dial. Now make yourself a little table with temperatures in one column and the dial readings in the other column, so that you know what setting you need for each temperature.

Remember that the temperatures you have measured are those in the centre of the oven. If you use the top shelf the temperature will be higher. If you use the bottom shelf the temperature will be lower. There is sometimes as much as 50° or 60° difference between the temperature of the top and bottom shelves.

Electric cookers too should be calibrated. The dials usually have temperature markings, instead of numbers, but these should also be checked with a thermometer just as you would a gas oven. Another point – electric ovens do not show anything like the variation in temperatures between top and bottom as a gas oven, and you can in fact assume that the temperature you measure in the middle applies throughout.

The best way to make sure that the temperature is right is to have an oven thermometer on the same shelf as the food while it is cooking.

Seasonings

Many soups, sauces, and stews are improved by the use of a bouquet garni. This is a bunch of herbs which the chef often calls a faggot. A bouquet is made of parsley stalks, a sprig of thyme, and a bay leaf, tied together in muslin. You can also use one or more other herbs, such as a blade of mace, whole peppercorns, cloves, and cinnamon bark. You will, of course, find it simpler – but not so interesting – to use mixed dried herbs. Do however use this with discretion, for their flavour is powerful – and long lasting ! The tiniest pinch is what you need.

Mustard, properly used, is the ideal accompaniment for many dishes. But never add dry mustard to sauces or dressings which are to be cooked. Make up the mustard at least an hour before you need it; the flavour developed in this way is quite different.

Freshly milled pepper has a flavour far superior to pepper sold already ground. Money invested in a small pepper mill is money invested wisely. Sea salt seasons food very differently from cooking or table salt, and is worth searching for. Some continental grocers stock it, but make sure it is for table use.

Cream

Whipped cream is an important ingredient in many cold sweets. In order to give a foam, cream must contain at least twenty per cent of fat. Single cream has a minimum fat content of eighteen per cent. It often contains as much as twenty-four per cent, but even so it cannot be used for whipped cream because it is homogenized in the dairy. The best foam is given by cream containing thirty to thirty-five per cent of fat. Double cream contains at least forty-eight per cent of fat and will whip. It is apt, however, to be dense and not well-aerated. If it is mixed with an equal volume of single cream, or one-third of its volume of fresh milk, it gives an excellent foam of good volume, and both mixtures contain about thirty-three per cent fat.

Recipes in this book which stipulate 'cream for whipping' can be made with double cream, perhaps diluted. The best temperature at which to whip cream is 40°–45° Fahrenheit. This is the temperature at which most domestic refrigerators run on the 'normal' setting. Cream at refrigerator temperature whips up to a larger volume than cream at room temperature. The reverse is true of white of egg which should be left at room temperature for some time before whipping.

Whenever whipped cream, beaten egg-white, or other aerated ingredients have to be added to a dish they should be 'folded' in with great care (to prevent air being driven out). The best utensil for the purpose is a metal tablespoon. It should be drawn through the mixture with slow, regular movements, always keeping the edge of the spoon as a cutting tool. If the bowl of the spoon is drawn across the mixture some air will be lost and a dense texture results.

Evaporated milk can be used for sweets requiring whipped cream. It has a distinct flavour, and it gives a very large volume. It whips more satisfactorily if two holes are punched in the top of the tin and the tin is then placed in a pan of boiling water for twenty minutes. After this it should be cooled and left in a refrigerator for several hours before use.

Gelatine

When gelatine has to be dissolved for use in creams, mousses, and soufflés, it should stand in the correct amount of cold water for five minutes to soften, and should then be heated over hot water until all the crystals have been dissolved. Before adding it to the mixture, test its temperature. If a thermometer is available, use the gelatine at 120° Fahrenheit. If there is no thermometer, insert the tip of the little finger, and the gelatine should feel a little warmer than blood heat but not hot. If it is used when hot it will warm the mixture to which it is added and any air whipped into cream, for example, will expand and produce coarse bubbles. If the gelatine is too cool, it will set into solid ropes as it meets the cold mixture.

Oils

Seed and nut oils are satisfactory for cooking and are cheaper than olive oil, but nothing can replace the flavour of a first-grade olive oil in the preparation of mayonnaise and when dressing salads with oil and vinegar.

Fats

From the nutritional point of view margarine and butter are interchangeable. So you can use margarine in most recipes which give butter. Butter can, of course, replace margarine at all times if the flavour is preferred. There are recipes in which butter is required for flavour or must be used because it is to be browned by heat; for example, brown butter sauce.

Clarified fat is required for many purposes in the kitchen. To clarify butter or margarine, melt it over a slow heat and continue to warm until splashing ceases. Do not allow it to become over-heated. Remove the pan from the flame and allow the fat to settle. With a metal spoon, remove any froth from the top and sediment from the bottom of the pan, so that the clear oil which remains can be used as clarified fat.

Sauces and thickenings

Whenever *hot* liquids are thickened with starch or with egg, care must be taken to prevent the starchy sauce becoming lumpy or the egg from coagulating and giving a curdled sauce.

If starch is used for thickening it should be blended with a little cold liquid (milk, water, or stock, according to the recipe) and then a little of the hot liquid from the pan should be poured on to it – stirring well meanwhile. The whole is then poured into the pan and stirred until boiling. This ensures that the starch grains are distributed throughout the mixture and do not form lumps.

When eggs are used, the contents of the pan must be allowed to cool a little and then some of the hot liquid is poured on to the beaten eggs, stirring all the time. The egg mixture is returned to the pan and stirred over a low heat until the egg thickens. It must not boil, or the egg will set and the sauce will curdle. This procedure takes longer to write than to execute, so that it has been omitted from the recipes in this book on the assumption that the cook will practise it. This method should always be used. A good rule in cooking is 'add hot to cold'.

Some sauces are thickened with uncooked flour and butter (or margarine) which have been worked together in a small basin with a fork or wooden spoon. Small pieces of this *beurre manié* are dropped into the boiling sauce and stirred until it becomes smooth and thick.

Lemon garnishes

Lemon butterflies are often used to garnish fish dishes. To make these butterflies, cut paper-thin slices across a lemon. Divide each slice into equal halves and remove any pips. Make an incision in the centre of each half-slice but do not cut completely in two pieces. Separate the two quarter circles of rind; they remain attached together by the central flesh but form a butterfly shape.

Half a lemon is often used to garnish a whole fish on a large dish. This has a better appearance if the cut edge of the rind is serrated with pointed scissors.

Sieving

When sieving soups and sauces a hair sieve and a nylon sieve are interchangeable. These divide food so finely that a really bland result is obtained. Wire sieves usually have a coarser mesh (various grades are sold) and are useful for making a purée of spinach or for a brown vegetable soup. Wire should not be used for tomatoes and other acid fruits which may react with the metal and change in flavour. 'Sieving' implies rubbing solid food through the mesh of the sieve. 'Straining' implies reserving the liquid and discarding the solid. Consommé is strained through tammy cloth. This is closely woven and is made of fabric rather like flannel. It retains any particles of food and gives a clear soup. If no tammy cloth is available, linen can be used. The cloth should be washed perfectly clean after use and scalded with boiling water before use.

Soufflé cases

To prepare a case for a hot soufflé, take a piece of greaseproof paper and fold into a strip of at least double thickness and long enough to encircle the soufflé case. It should be deep enough to project two to three inches above the rim of the case. Tie this securely with string so that the paper is not crumpled. Grease inside the paper and the soufflé case.

For a cold soufflé, greasing is not necessary and a better result is given by cartridge paper which is stiff enough to retain a smooth outline. Any creases in the paper cause the edge of the mixture to be uneven in outline. Aluminium foil gives an equally good result and is easier to handle than paper.

Flavourings

Lemon or orange rind are frequently grated or cut thinly to flavour sweets. In no circumstances should any of the white pith be included, or a bitter flavour will result. It is the 'zest' or coloured portion which should be used. This is a very thin layer, and if it is shaved off with a sharp knife it should be possible to see the knife blade through the zest.

Vanilla essence is commonly used for flavouring, but a vanilla pod gives an infinitely more pleasant result. The pod is infused in warm milk for half an hour, and the milk is then used to prepare a custard or other basic mixture. The pod can be washed, dried, and kept for future use.

Blanching meats

White meats, brains, and sweetbread are frequently blanched before cooking. To blanch meat, place it in a pan and cover it with cold water. Bring the water gradually to boiling point, and then pour it away. Cover the meat with cold water and allow it to stand until cold.

Cutting vegetables

Vegetables are cut into various shapes for different purposes. A mirepoix of vegetables is used in the base of a braising

pot and supports the meat or other piece of food which is to
be braised. The pieces of vegetable need not be cut into neat
shapes, and should be one inch or more on all sides, since
their function is to keep the chief ingredients above the
level of the stock. A julienne of vegetables is cut to garnish
consommé julienne, braised sweetbreads, and certain other
dishes. Vegetables for this purpose should be cut no larger
than, and the same shape as, a matchstick. A brunoise of
vegetables is composed of perfectly shaped dice a little larger
than a small green pea. The simplest way to cut julienne or
brunoise is to trim each vegetable to a rectangular shape, cut
the rectangle into slices of identical thickness, pile two or
three slices on top of each other, and slice the pile into
identical strips. The strips form a julienne, and if they are
cut across to give dice the result is a brunoise.

Browned breadcrumbs

Crusts and pieces of stale bread can be dried in a slow oven,
crushed between two sheets of clean paper, and rubbed
through a wire sieve to produce 'browned crumbs' or 'bread
raspings'. These give a crisp crust to foods which are to be
grilled or reheated in a quick oven. They can also be used
with egg to coat foods before frying them in deep fat.

Raspings will store for a long time in an airtight jar or tin.

Wine and wine vinegar

Wine improves soups and sauces and stocks. Inferior and
cooking wines should be cooked for a long time or their taste
will be rough. A good table sherry can be added to soups
just before serving.

Wine vinegar and cider vinegar have a place in the store-
cupboard. (Sour wine and flat cider can be used up in some
strongly flavoured stews.) A wine merchant will sell good
wine vinegar. Tarragon vinegar, chilli vinegar, and other
herb vinegars improve many sauces based on mayonnaise.

'A *spoonful*'

All the tablespoons and teaspoons in this book are assumed
to be filled only until level with the edge. The most accurate
way to do this is to lift up a heaped spoonful and draw a
knife across the edge (touching the metal all the way), to
cut off the surplus. What remains is a level spoonful.

CHAPTER 1

Soups

THE English are not a very soup-conscious nation, though the Scots do appreciate the value of a good, appetizing soup. Most thin soups have little direct nutritional value, but they form an excellent and appetizing introduction to a meal. Increasingly we tend to get our soup from tins or packets, and there is nothing at all wrong with this. But most people will agree that nothing has the flavour and aroma of a good home-made soup.

The recipes which follow are of course for soups which do not have too much carbohydrate. And if the soup is one which goes well with a garnish of rice or noodles, there is no reason why the other members of your family, or your guests, should be deprived of the garnish just because you do not want any.

A well-flavoured, well-seasoned stock is the basis of a good soup; a chop bone simmered in a quart of water will not make a satisfactory understudy. Brown stock, white stock, vegetable stock, fish stock, or, in some cases, half stock and half milk are required. There is also a place for the soup cube available from the grocery store if it is used instead of stock. To this, the remaining ingredients are added and the whole is simmered long enough to extract the full flavour from everything in the pan, and to render it tender. Unnecessary and prolonged cooking not only wastes fuel, but it impairs the final flavour. The recipes for various stocks appear on pages 28, 48, 49, and 50.

ARTICHOKE SOUP

INGREDIENTS: 4 portions

1 lb. Jerusalem artichokes	¼ pt milk
1 onion	1 tablesp. cream
1 stalk celery	½ oz. cornflour
1 oz. butter	Bouquet garni
1 pt white stock	Pepper and salt

METHOD

Wash the artichokes and peel under water. Have a little lemon juice or vinegar in the water to prevent the vegetables from darkening. Wash the celery and peel the onion. Slice all the vegetables thinly and place in a heavy pan. Add the butter and cook gently for 15 minutes with a lid on the pan. Shake at intervals to prevent burning. Add the stock, bouquet garni, and seasoning, and bring rapidly to the boil. Reduce the heat and simmer gently until all the vegetables are tender. This takes 20–30 minutes. Rub through a nylon sieve and return to the washed pan. Blend the cornflour with the cold milk and add to the soup. Stir continuously until boiling and boil for 2–3 minutes. Add the cream, correct the seasoning, and serve.

BISQUES

Bisques are shellfish soups and should never be over-cooked.

BISQUE OF LOBSTER

INGREDIENTS: 3 portions

Half a small cooked lobster	Salt and pepper (preferably
1 pt fish stock (see p. 50)	cayenne)
1 oz. butter	2 tablesps. cream
¾ oz. rice- or cornflour	2 tablesps. good sherry

½ an onion
slice of carrot
Bouquet garni (be very sparing with thyme)

Lemon juice and lobster butter, i.e. ½ oz. butter and ½ oz. of lobster coral rubbed through a hair sieve

METHOD

Prepare the vegetables, remove the lobster meat from the shell, and break the shell. Place one ounce of butter in a heavy pan and cook the sliced carrot and onion in it gently for 15 minutes with the lid on the pan. Shake frequently. Remove the lid and gently work in the rice-flour or cornflour and then, by degrees, add the stock. Toss in the broken shell, bouquet garni, and seasoning. Add most of the lobster meat cut finely but reserve a few dice to garnish the soup. Bring to the boil and then simmer for 30 minutes. Rub through a hair sieve. Return to the pan, reheat but do not boil. Stir in cream and then sherry and lastly whisk the lobster butter in. Add the diced lobster and serve. This soup should take a pale pink colour from the lobster butter.

Other shellfish may be used in place of lobster and give their names to the bisque.

BORTSCH

INGREDIENTS: 5–6 portions

1½ pts of good brown stock, preferably made with shin of beef
1½ lb. cooked beetroot
1 small dark-red raw beetroot

2 teasps. vinegar
Sour cream
Pepper, salt, and a pinch of sugar

METHOD

Peel the raw beetroot, grate it finely, and mix with the vinegar. Peel the cooked beetroot and cut into tiny chips. Bring the stock to the boil and season well, drop in the cooked beetroot and boil for only 1–2 minutes in order to retain a good colour. Squeeze the raw beetroot and vinegar in muslin and add the juice to the soup. Taste and add a little sugar if required. Serve with tablespoons of sour cream in the soup bowl, or serve the cream separately.

Small meat patties of puff pastry usually accompany bortsch, or tartlets containing cream cheese.

BOUILLABAISSE

Many kinds of fish are required for a good bouillabaisse, so it is not worth making unless six or eight people are to share it. Nevertheless, it is a novelty in England, and novel foods are generally appreciated. On the Mediterranean shore of France it is a local speciality. True, there are fish in that part of the world which are not available to us, but we can produce a palatable soup from our own fish.

INGREDIENTS: 6–8 portions

2 whitings
2 red mullets
One cup of lobster or craw-fish meat
2 large cutlets of John Dory or sea bream or 1 medium-sized Dover sole, or
2 lb. of fish such as turbot, bream, whiting, eel, carp, or haddock
3 onions
¼ lb. tomatoes (skin and seeds removed)

¼ pt of white wine
1 bay leaf
1½ in. of leek
½ lemon
Pinch of saffron
2 oz. oil
Pepper and salt
1 clove of garlic
Water
Chopped parsley
(2 to 3 cloves are sometimes added)

METHOD

Cut the fish into large pieces. Take a heavy shallow pan, and heat in it the oil. Chop the onions finely and cook gently in oil until light brown. Add the fish and barely cover with water. Throw into the pan a muslin bag containing a thin sliver of lemon zest, the bay leaf, and a crushed clove of garlic. Add the tomato pulp, the juice from half a lemon, the chopped leek, the wine, chopped parsley, pepper, and salt. Bring quickly to the boil and then lower the heat and simmer for 15 – 20 minutes but no longer. Remove the muslin bag. Stir in a pinch of saffron. Serve the whole in one large dish; alternatively, serve the soup in a tureen and the fish on a dish with prawns to garnish it. Thin slices of French bread are usually placed in the bottom of the tureen.

FRESHWATER BOUILLABAISSE

Although the purist would not concede that bouillabaisse can be made without the correct fish, the British angler may wish to use his catch to make a freshwater version of this dish.

Bream is too slimy and chub has too much bone to be included, but pike, perch, roach, rudd, dace, bleak, eels, and gudgeon are all suitable fish.

With a couple of pounds of fish you need two good onions, sliced, four tomatoes, skinned and crushed, a clove of garlic, a bay leaf, a pinch of saffron, parsley, and fennel, and enough olive oil to cover the pieces of fish.

Cut the fish into pieces, fairly small, some smaller than others, and separate the softer from the firmer. Put the firmer bits of fish, and all the trimmings, into a pan and just cover the fish with oil. Then pour boiling water over the whole lot and cook fairly furiously for 5 minutes.

Now add the softer fish pieces, and a glass of white wine, and boil the lot hard for 7 minutes more.

To serve, pour off the liquid into soup bowls containing bits of bread: fried, toasted, or merely baked. Put the fish, into a dish and sprinkle with parsley. Serve both at once, the liquid and the fish.

CAULIFLOWER SOUP

INGREDIENTS: 4–6 portions

1 small cauliflower	¾ pt milk
1 small onion	¾ oz. ground rice, cornflour,
Bouquet garni	or flour
Pepper and salt	Pinch of grated nutmeg
3 or 4 tablesps. cream	¾ oz. butter
¾ pt white stock	

METHOD

Wash the cauliflower and plunge into boiling water for 2 minutes. Drain it, and remove a few small sprigs for garnishing. Chop the remainder and chop the onion. Cook these slowly in butter for 10–15 minutes with a lid on the pan. Add the stock, bouquet garni, and seasoning, and bring quickly to the boil. Lower the heat and simmer gently for 35 minutes. Rub through a nylon sieve. Blend the ground rice with the milk and pour on to them the sieved soup. Return to the pan, stir until boiling and boil gently until the rice is clear. Cook the sprigs of cauliflower which are intended as a garnish in boiling salted water. Drain them and place into a serving tureen. Correct the seasoning of the soup and remove from the flame. Stir in three or four tablespoonfuls of cream or top milk and pour over the cauliflower sprigs.

CELERY SOUP

INGREDIENTS: 4–6 portions

1 head of celery	¾ oz. butter
1 onion	¾ oz. flour
Bouquet garni	6 peppercorns

| 1 pt white stock | Salt |
| 1/2 pt milk | 3 tablesps. cream |

METHOD

Wash the celery, peel the onion, and chop them together. Melt the butter in a stewpan, add the vegetables, and put on the lid. Sauté gently for 15 minutes, shaking the pan at intervals. Add the stock, seasoning, and bouquet garni, and bring quickly to the boil. Lower the heat and simmer about 30 minutes or until tender. Rub through a nylon sieve. Blend the flour with milk in a clean pan, add the sieved soup, and stir until boiling. Boil for 3 minutes. Correct the seasoning and consistency, remove from the stove, and stir in cream.

Celeriac can be used in place of celery: 4–6 oz. makes one pint of soup.

CHERRY SOUP

INGREDIENTS: 4–6 portions

1 lb. cherries	1 1/2 pts of stock
1 very small onion	1 wine-glass of port or claret
1 tomato or a small piece of lemon zest	1/2 oz. sugar
	Red colouring
Small piece of celery	1 tablesp. arrowroot
3 cloves	Pepper and salt
Small piece of bay leaf	

METHOD

Stone the cherries and reserve a few for garnishing the soup. Crack a few of the stones and tie them in muslin. Prepare and slice the vegetables and place them in a pan with the cherries, stock, cloves, bay leaf, sugar, and crushed stones. Bring to the boil and cook for 30–40 minutes. Strain, and add the blended arrowroot and wine. Stir until boiling, add red colouring if necessary, and add the cherries reserved for garnish.

CHICKEN BROTH

INGREDIENTS: 8–10 portions approx.

1 chicken
1 small onion
Salt and pepper
A small blade of mace

1 tablesp. finely chopped
*   parsley*
Up to 4 pts water (according
*   to size of the chicken)*

METHOD

Cut the chicken into pieces and break the bones. Scald and
skin the feet, wash the giblets and add them to the pan.
Cover all with water, add salt, and bring to the boil. Remove
scum, add pepper, mace, and onion, and simmer gently for 3–4
hours. Strain. If possible, allow to get cold and lift the solidified fat from the top. If this is not possible, skim the fat off
the hot broth with a spoon and absorbent kitchen paper.
Reheat, correct seasoning, add chopped parsley, and serve.

One tablespoonful of washed and blanched rice may be
added to the strained soup which must then be boiled another 15 or 20 minutes.

In Bulgaria, chicken soup is served with tiny cubes of
white meat and liver in it, and just before serving a knob
of butter, a little lemon juice, and beaten egg yolks are stirred
in. The soup must not be boiling or the eggs will curdle.

COCK-A-LEEKIE

INGREDIENTS: 8–10 portions

1 small boiling fowl
1 carrot
1 turnip
1 lb. young leeks, trimmed
*   and cut into very short*
*   lengths*

1 onion
1 tablesp. finely chopped
*   parsley*
3–4 pts water
2 or 3 cloves
1 tablesp. rice

METHOD

Put the trussed fowl in a stewpan and cover with water. Add
salt and bring it to the boil. Remove the scum and add pepper,
and peeled, sliced carrot and turnip. Peel the onion, stick
the cloves in it and put it in the pot. Cook 3–4 hours, until
the fowl is tender. Strain the broth into a clean pan and
add the rice and leeks which have been washed and scalded.
Boil for 20–30 minutes. Meanwhile, dice some of the flesh
from the fowl and, when the soup is ready to serve, taste
it for seasoning, put in the meat and chopped parsley and
pour into a serving bowl.

CONSOMMÉ

Consommé is a clarified stock with a very good flavour.

All consommés can be made from one recipe, and, according to the garnish added, so the name will vary. The garnish
should be cooked separately and put into the serving bowl
just before the soup is poured in.

CONSOMMÉ JULIENNE: Thin match-sized strips of carrot,
turnip, leek, and lettuce.

CONSOMMÉ BRUNOISE: Tiny diced root vegetables and
peas.

CONSOMMÉ AU RIZ: Plain boiled rice.

CONSOMMÉ ROYALE: Custard of egg and stock covered
with spinach, tomato, etc., and cut into fancy shapes after
cooking.

CONSOMMÉ BAVIÈRE: Small semolina quenelles.

CONSOMMÉ CHIFFONADE: Lettuce and sorrel finely
shredded and also quenelles sprinkled with chervil.

Consommé must be made from a specially prepared strong

stock or bouillon and cannot be made from ordinary household bone stock. Because the final result must be crystal clear, the consommé is cooked with lean minced beef, chicken carcases or giblets, egg white and crushed egg shells, and preferably coarse grey salt. These ingredients all clarify the soup but even when they are used they may not give a perfect result if a cloudy stock is employed. Firstly, then, the stock must be made.

INGREDIENTS

4 qts of water	1 small turnip
6 peppercorns	1 carrot
1 teasp. salt	1 onion
1 lb. knuckle of veal	1 stick of celery
3 lb. shin of beef	

METHOD

Saw up the bones and remove any fat. Shred the meat into fine pieces and discard all fat. Prepare and cut up the vegetables. Put the meat, bones, and water into a large pan with salt, and bring to the boil. Remove scum as it rises. When boiling, add the vegetables and simmer at least 5 hours. Strain through a nylon sieve and leave until cold. Remove all fat before use.

QUENELLES are made from meat, fish, game, or chicken which has been pounded in a mortar and diluted with white of egg and cream. After seasoning well and chilling over ice the mixture is divided into very small portions, poached in boiling water, drained, and used.

CONSOMMÉ: RECIPE 1 (ECONOMICAL)

INGREDIENTS: 6–8 portions

1 qt consommé stock	1 turnip
¼ lb. lean beef	1 onion

⅛ pt cold water
White and shell of 1 egg
6 white peppercorns
1 carrot

1 dessertsp. sherry
A bouquet garni plus 1 clove
   and a little blade mace
½ teasp. Bovril

METHOD

Remove fat and sinew from meat and shred very finely.
Cover it with the cold water and soak for 30 minutes. Scald
a pan and a whisk with boiling water. Add the meat, lightly
whisked egg white, crushed egg shell, vegetables, herbs, and
de-greased stock. Stir well and whisk over a slow heat until
almost boiling. Reduce the heat and simmer very gently for
30 minutes. Strain through a scalded tammy cloth. Strain
again if not perfectly clear. Reheat, add the Bovril, sherry,
and prepared garnish.

CONSOMMÉ: RECIPE 2

INGREDIENTS: 6–8 portions

1qt consommé stock
½ lb. shin of beef
¼ lb. crushed tomato
Chicken carcase or giblets
   (crushed or broken)
2 oz. carrot
⅛ pt sherry
¼ stick of celery

¼ oz. coarse salt
3 white peppercorns
Thyme, bay leaf, and 1 small
   clove of garlic all tied in
   muslin
1 leek
White and shell of 1 egg
1 tablesp. good sherry

METHOD

Mince or shred the beef and put all the ingredients except
stock, chicken, and tomatoes into a scalded pan. Add a little
stock and mix well to break up the egg white. Add chicken.
Slowly pour on the warm stock, whisking meanwhile. Add
the tomatoes and bring slowly to the boil, whisking frequently. When the whites rise to the top, whisking can stop.

Remove from the flame immediately it boils and heat below
boiling point for 2 hours. Strain through a scalded tammy
cloth. Season and reboil before serving. Add a little gravy
browning to give a pale amber colour and stir in a glass of
good sherry immediately before serving.

The soup must reach boiling point and then cook at a lower
temperature to extract the full flavour from all the ingredients. If it continued to boil it would be cloudy.

CUCUMBER SOUP

INGREDIENTS: 4–5 portions

1 large cucumber
1½ pts white or vegetable
   stock
1 teasp. chopped onion
¾ oz. butter

¾ oz. flour
1 teasp. chopped mint
Green colouring
Pepper and salt

METHOD

Peel the cucumber and reserve a little of it to garnish the
soup. This portion should be chopped finely or grated. Cut
the remaining cucumber into thin slices and place it in the
stock, together with the chopped onion and seasoning. Bring
it to the boil and then simmer slowly for 20 minutes. Rub
through a nylon sieve. Melt the butter, stir in the flour, and
gradually work in the cucumber stock. Stir until boiling
and boil gently for 3 minutes. Add colouring and correct
seasoning, stir in the grated raw cucumber and chopped mint,
and serve. This soup is much improved if three tablespoons
of cream are added at the last moment and it can be thickened
further by working in two beaten egg yolks after it has
cooled a little.

HARE SOUP

INGREDIENTS: 8–10 portions

3 pts brown stock	Small piece of celery
½ a hare	Bouquet garni
1 oz. butter	Salt
1 oz. flour or cornflour	6 peppercorns
1 onion	1 wine-glass of port
1 carrot	1 tablesp. redcurrant jelly
1 small turnip	

METHOD

Wipe the hare and cut into small pieces. Wash, peel, and cut
up the vegetables. Melt the butter in a stewpan and fry the
hare and vegetables until well browned. Add the stock, bouquet garni, and the peppercorns, and bring quickly to the
boil. Skim. Lower the heat and simmer for 2½–3 hours. Remove the meat from the bones and rub it through a sieve.
Strain the stock off the vegetables, and place stock and sieved
meat in a stewpan. Blend the cornflour and wine and pour
into the soup. Add the redcurrant jelly and stir until boiling.
Boil gently for 3 minutes. Taste for seasoning and add a little
gravy browning if necessary.

If there is any blood from the hare, reserve it before making
the soup. Add vinegar in the proportion of one tablespoon
of vinegar to quarter of a pint of blood to prevent it coagulating. When the soup is ready to serve take it off the heat, cool
a little, and stir in the blood.

HOLLANDAISE SOUP

INGREDIENTS: 3–4 portions

1 pt white or vegetable stock	1 tablesp. green peas
	1 cucumber

⅛ pt milk   1 carrot
⅛ pt cream   Pepper and salt
½ oz. butter   Yolk of 2 eggs
½ oz. flour

METHOD

Prepare the vegetables and dice the carrot and the cucumber until approximately the size of peas, or, better still, use a small scoop to produce tiny 'peas' of each vegetable. Cook these in boiling salted water. Melt the butter, stir in the flour, and gradually work in one pint of stock and add seasoning. Stir until boiling and boil gently for ten minutes. Remove from the stove, whisk the egg yolks and milk together, and pour on to them the slightly cooled soup. Pour through a strainer into the pan and stir over a slow heat until the yolks thicken, but do not allow to boil. Add the cooked vegetables and cream. Correct seasoning and serve.

JELLIED SOUPS

Consommé made with a good stock and more veal bone than usual will set to a very light jelly when cold, and makes a refreshing opening course to a summer meal. A slice or a quarter of lemon is always served with each bowl of soup. The recipes for consommé may be used for this purpose and it is very easy to test in advance whether the soup will gel when cold by the simple means of making the stock the previous day and leaving it overnight, when it should set lightly. Jellied soups should not be stiff. If the soup is not gelatinous enough, a teaspoonful of gelatine may be added to the soup – but it is not advisable to depend on added gelatine since this destroys the typical consistency and impairs the flavour. Cold consommé should not be iced but it should be very cold.

KIDNEY SOUP

INGREDIENTS: 4–5 portions

4 oz. kidney
1 small carrot
Piece of turnip
1 onion
1 tablesp. cornflour
Small glass of sherry or red
 wine

1 oz. dripping
1½ pts brown stock
Bouquet garni plus a pinch
 of mace
Salt and pepper
Gravy browning
Meat extract if necessary

METHOD

Wash and skin the kidneys and remove the core. Prepare and
slice the vegetables, slice the kidney. Melt the dripping in a
stewpan and fry the kidney and vegetables until brown. Add
the stock, wine, and bouquet garni and simmer 45 minutes,
allowing the volume to reduce to about one pint. Remove a
little kidney and chop it for garnishing the soup, rub the
rest of the ingredients through a fine wire sieve.

Blend the cornflour with a little cold stock, add the sieved
soup and stir until boiling. Correct the seasoning and add
gravy browning to give a good colour. A little meat extract
may be required. Stir in the chopped kidney before serving.

MINESTRONE

This Italian soup is packed with vegetables and represents a
meal in itself. Macaroni is usually broken into tiny pieces
and cooked in it and many recipes include haricot beans.

INGREDIENTS: 6–8 portions

1 carrot
2 peeled tomatoes

2 pts stock or water
Salt and pepper

1 onion

2 sticks of celery

1 small leek – white only

½ small turnip

2 oz. peas

2 oz. broad beans

2 oz. cabbage

2 oz. bacon

1 clove garlic (optional)

2 oz. French beans

Basil and any fresh herbs available, e.g. thyme, chives, and marjoram

2 oz. haricot beans ⎫
2 oz. macaroni ⎬ Optional
⎭

1 tablesp. chopped parsley

3 oz. grated cheese

METHOD

Soak the haricot beans overnight and then simmer in stock until three-quarters cooked. Trim the bacon and cut into small squares. Prepare the vegetables and chop into small pieces. Fry the bacon slowly until the fat runs out. Add the onion (and crushed clove of garlic) and fry until golden brown. Add the stock, herbs, and all the vegetables except cabbage, peas, and French or broad beans. Bring to the boil and then simmer for 15 minutes. Add the marcaroni, French beans, shredded cabbage, broad beans, and peas and cook another 15–20 minutes. Correct the seasoning, sprinkle with parsley, and serve with grated cheese.

Almost any vegetable in season can be added to this soup, including asparagus tips, cauliflower, baby marrow, potatoes, aubergines, mushrooms, and marrows. Any tiny pasta shapes, rice, or noodles can replace marcaroni.

In some regions cheese is served separately and in others it is stirred into the soup. Whichever method is employed the cheese should be Parmesan. Whole smoked sausage is sometimes cooked in the soup and diced just before serving. This soup has a remarkably good flavour even if the haricot beans and pasta are omitted. Frozen peas and broad beans can be used for minestrone, but need only be cooked for 5–8 minutes in order to make them tender.

MOCKTURTLE SOUP

INGREDIENTS: 6–8 portions

1 qt brown stock	*Turtle tea*
2 oz. carrot	*Calves' head and calves' foot*
2 oz. onion	*Diced carrot and turnip to*
2 oz. bacon trimmings or rinds (not too fatty)	*garnish*
3 oz. flour	*Pepper and salt*
2 oz. dripping	*Bouquet garni*

METHOD

Prepare and dice the vegetables and bacon. Fry until brown in the dripping and then remove from the pan and keep hot. Add the flour to the hot dripping and stir over a high flame until pale chocolate brown. Remove from the stove and immediately stir in the stock. Replace the fried vegetables and add the bouquet garni and seasoning. Bring to the boil and then lower the heat and simmer gently for 1½ hours. Add more stock to allow for evaporation. Pour through a strainer into a clean pan and add turtle tea to flavour. Re-boil, adjust seasoning, and stir in some diced cooked calves' head or calves' foot and quarter-inch cubes of cooked carrots and turnip.

TURTLE TEA: a little boiling stock and a pinch each of rosemary, basil, marjoram, savory, thyme with a very small piece of bayleaf, and a soupçon of mace are put into a pan; do not heat. Infuse the herbs in the stock for ten minutes only and strain immediately. Use as required.

MULLIGATAWNY SOUP

INGREDIENTS: 6–8 portions

1 qt brown stock	1 teasp. chutney
1 dessertsp. curry powder and curry paste mixed	½ oz. desiccated or grated fresh coconut

(this amount can be
doubled if liked)

¾ oz. flour

1 oz. dripping

4 oz. onion or shallot

1 oz. plain boiled rice

1 teasp. tamarind juice

1 dessertsp. tomato purée

4 oz. chopped apple

Salt

METHOD

Shred the onion finely and fry in dripping until light brown. Add the flour and curry and stir over a flame until of a sandy texture. Gradually add stock, tomato purée, and then apple, chutney, coconut, tamarind, seasoning, and a little lemon juice. Bring to the boil and then lower the heat and simmer gently for an hour. Skim occasionally. Pour through a strainer into a clean pan and bring to the boil. Correct seasoning, add more lemon juice if necessary, and adjust consistency. Serve with plain boiled rice as a garnish and pass lemon quarters with the soup.

MULLIGATAWNY SOUP (CLEAR)

INGREDIENTS: 6–8 portions

1 qt stock

4 oz. lean beef

1 gill water

1 tablesp. curry powder

1 teasp. curry-paste

1 onion or 2 shallots

1 small carrot

2 oz. chopped apple

Salt

Lemon juice

1 egg white and egg shell

2 oz. cooked chicken for
garnish

METHOD

Shred the beef and soak in the water for 15 minutes with the curry powder and paste. Put all the ingredients into a scalded pan on a slow heat and whisk until almost boiling. Lower the heat once it boils and then simmer slowly for 30 minutes.

Strain through a scalded tammy cloth. Correct seasoning and reheat with two ounces of diced cooked chicken in the soup. Serve with plain boiled rice.

MUSHROOM SOUP

INGREDIENTS: 3–4 portions

8 oz. *mushrooms* or 1 lb. *stalks*	1 teasp. *salt*
1 pt *chicken stock*	*Pepper and grated nutmeg*
1 oz. *butter*	3 tablesps. *cream*
	2 egg yolks

METHOD

Wash and slice the mushrooms and place in a small stewpan with the butter. Cover with a lid and cook gently for 10 minutes, shaking the pan at intervals. Add the stock and seasoning, bring to the boil, lower the heat, and simmer for 20 to 30 minutes. Remove a few pieces of mushroom and dice neatly to serve in the soup. Rub the remaining ingredients through a fine sieve or grind them in an electric blender until smooth. Return to the pan and reheat. Correct the seasoning. Remove the pan from the stove and cool the soup slightly. Beat up the egg yolks and cream together, and stir into the soup. Reheat gently to thicken the soup but do not boil. Add the diced mushroom and serve.

ONION SOUP

INGREDIENTS: 4–6 portions

½ lb. *onions*	A small piece of bay leaf and
1½ oz. *butter*	a scrap of blade mace
½ oz. *flour*	*Pepper and salt*
1½ pts *white or vegetable stock*	1½ oz. *grated cheese*
	French bread

METHOD

Chop the onion very finely and brown slowly in the butter. Sprinkle in the flour and fry until faintly golden. Gradually stir in the boiling stock. Add the herbs and simmer for 30 minutes. Remove herbs. Put two or three small slices of French bread (toasted or plain) in an earthenware casserole and pour the soup on to them. Sprinkle grated cheese on top of the dish and brown under the grill.

OXTAIL SOUP (CLEAR)

INGREDIENTS: 8–10 portions

½ oxtail	Bouquet garni
2 pts white consommé stock	6 white peppercorns
1 pt water	Salt
4 oz. carrot	½ lb. minced lean beef
4 oz. turnip	1 egg white and shell
4 oz. onion	1 leek – white part only
2 sticks of celery	

GARNISH: Cooked diced celery and oxtail and small balls of cooked carrot and turnip.

METHOD

Wipe the oxtail and cut into sections. Put the meat and vegetables, bouquet garni, and seasoning into a pan with stock and water. Bring to the boil and skim. Lower the heat and simmer for 5–6 hours. Strain and then allow to get cold and remove the fat. Reheat and clear with minced beef, leek, and egg as for consommé and strain through a tammy cloth. Garnish with some of the diced meat and cooked celery, carrot, and turnip. A glass of good sherry improves this soup.

OXTAIL SOUP (THICK)

INGREDIENTS: 6–8 portions

1 qt stock	1 oz. lean ham or bacon
½ oxtail	Bouquet garni
4 oz. onion	6 peppercorns
4 oz. carrot	Salt
2 oz. turnip	1 tablesp. cornflour
2 stalks celery	1 small glass of sherry
1 oz. margarine or dripping	

METHOD

Wipe and joint the tail and roll the joints in the seasoned flour. Dice the ham. Prepare and dice the vegetables. Melt the fat in a stewpan and fry these ingredients until brown. Add the stock and peppercorns and bouquet garni, and bring to the boil. Skim, reduce the heat, and simmer about 5 hours. Pour through a strainer and skim the fat off the soup; if it is allowed to cool overnight the fat can be lifted off the top very easily. Blend the cornflour and sherry together and add to the soup. Stir until boiling. Correct the seasoning and consistency, and serve with some of the diced flesh from the oxtail in the soup bowl.

This soup can also be made from left-over oxtail stew. A quart of oxtail stock and about four ounces of meat from the tail form the chief ingredients. A little lean cooked bacon or ham improves the flavour. The meat should be chopped or minced and rubbed through a sieve, and the stock added to it. The stock must have a good flavour and should be free from grease. An ounce of butter, margarine, or dripping and an ounce of flour should be made into a roux and sieved meat and stock added, and the whole stirred until boiling. Seasoning and a glass of sherry should be added before serving. If thickened gravy from the stew is used instead of stock, you will need little if any flour and butter.

POT AU FEU

This is a French household soup made from ribs of beef and forming the basis of many other soups.

INGREDIENTS: about 12 portions

1½ lb. rib of beef rolled	4 oz. leek
Bones from the rib	4 oz. cabbage
2 qts water	1 oz. celery
2 oz. carrots	1 oz. parsley
3 oz. onion stuck with 2 cloves	Bouquet garni
	12 peppercorns

METHOD

Tie up the beef and place in cold water. Bring to the boil and throw away the water. Slit the leeks lengthwise to clean them, and peel the root vegetables. Place the meat and bones in a clean saucepan and cover with water. Bring to the boil and skim. Add salt, peppercorns, and bouquet garni and simmer for 1 hour. Add the whole carrots and onions, and the leeks and cabbage tied with string. Simmer for another 3 hours. Remove the vegetables, strain the soup through a scalded tammy cloth, and leave until cold so that all the fat can be removed.

This soup can be made from brisket, chuck, topside, shoulder, neck, or bottom round of beef instead of rib. If a large quantity is being made it is wise to use two cuts of beef, one lean and one fatter. The meat can be served separately as boiled beef. If this is to be done it should be removed from the soup pot when it is cooked. The bones and vegetables can still simmer on their own. The bouillon produced by this means can be served as pot au feu or can form the basis of consommés or any soup based on a well-flavoured bouillon. Here is one:

CROUTE AU POT

A long French loaf is sliced and baked in the oven or toasted and then put in a serving bowl. The vegetables from the pot au feu are cut into neat dice and also put in the soup bowl. The soup is brought to the boil and poured over the vegetables.

QUICK SOUPS

Unexpected guests sometimes call when there is no stock available for soup making and sundry makeshift soups which can be prepared at a moment's notice are useful additions to a recipe book.

TOMATO SOUP

INGREDIENTS: 2 portions

1 tin of tomato juice	1 teasp. arrowroot or
1 clove of garlic squeezed in	cornflour blended with
a garlic press, or	⅛ pt water
1 thin slice of onion	Pepper, salt, and sugar

METHOD

Blend the starch with cold water, stir into the remaining ingredients and bring to the boil. Remove the garlic or onion and serve.

The emulsifying attachment to an electric mixer enables vegetables to be made into a purée in a matter of seconds. If they are then heated, with water, seasoning, and herbs, a soup can be prepared in less than 5 minutes. A soup cube may be added, too. Recipes for these soups are not really necessary. The proportion for a tomato soup would be the same as for a soup made by the normal method. The tomatoes and onions are mixed until creamy and then heated to boiling point. The flavour is improved by longer cooking, but the finely divided vegetable cooks quickly and flavours blend well when the whole is of a smooth and creamy texture.

Cold soups can be made this way and require no cooking at all. Green vegetables such as washed spinach and watercress can be mixed with mint, parsley, and onions to give a smooth purée which is seasoned to taste and diluted with water or stock. A little lemon juice often improves the flavour. Fresh or canned tomatoes mixed with either celery or onion or else made semi-sweet with apple or pineapple juice form excellent cold soups. Tomato always requires sugar to give it a full flavour.

There are also ingredients which cook so quickly that soups can be made almost instantaneously. Avocado pears for instance make an excellent soup.

AVOCADO SOUP: 2–3 portions

A finely chopped onion and two teaspoonfuls of chopped celery browned in one ounce of butter form the basis. A tablespoonful of flour is stirred in and cooked until light brown and then a pint of water or stock is added and a bouquet garni. This is simmered until the celery is tender and quarter of a pint of mashed avocado pulp is stirred in and cooked just for 5 minutes. The bouquet garni is removed and a tablespoonful or so of cream or top milk is stirred in. If the onion and celery are prepared in the electric blender they can be cooked very quickly.

PUMPKIN SOUP

Peel and cut up one pound of pumpkin and mash in the electric blender. Put the pulp in a saucepan and add a pint of scalded milk, a good knob of butter, and some pepper and salt. Add a little sugar if required and heat until boiling. Pumpkins lend themselves to many modifications of this recipe. (1) Water or diluted soup cube can be used in place of milk; (2) potato can be grated into the pan and cooked until tender in the soup; (3) rice can be boiled in milk and the whole added to the pumpkin purée; (4) onions and tomatoes can be added in varying proportions to give a totally different flavour. As with most white or pale coloured soups, some cream stirred in at the last moment improves the result very much and thickens the soup. Blended flour can be used for thickening if the consistency is not satisfactory.

Marrows can be used in place of pumpkins.

SCOTCH BROTH

INGREDIENTS: 10–12 portions

2 lb. best end of neck or shoulder of mutton	2 onions
1½ oz. pearl barley	¼ lb. green peas
¼ cabbage	4 pts water
2 carrots	Pepper and salt
1 turnip	1 tablesp. chopped parsley

METHOD

Scald the barley in boiling water, wipe the meat and remove excess fat. Put the meat and barley in a pan and add the water; bring to the boil. Skim, add seasoning, lower the heat, and simmer for 1 hour. Prepare and dice the vegetables and add them to the soup and simmer for another hour. The peas should be put in only for long enough to make them tender. Dice a little of the cooked meat and place into a soup tureen. Pour the soup with all the vegetables it contains into the tureen. Remove the fat from the top and sprinkle parsley over it. It is better to prepare this soup the day before it is required so that the fat can be lifted from the top when it is cold. Seasoning is important and Scotch broth requires a great deal of salt.

Mutton broth is merely Scotch broth without cabbage.

The mutton used to flavour this soup can be served as boiled mutton or made into various dishes requiring cooked meat.

SHRIMP SOUP

Prepare one and a half pints of fish stock by simmering the shrimp shells, some white fish trimmings, e.g. skin and bone of sole or plaice, with a slice of onion, a bouquet garni, and a thin strip of lemon zest for 20 minutes. Strain this stock, season well, and use for this soup.

INGREDIENTS: 4–6 portions

1 pt cooked shelled shrimps	3 tablesps. cream
1½ pts fish stock	1 egg yolk
1 oz. butter	Lemon juice
3 tablesps. breadcrumbs	Nutmeg
⅛ pt milk	

METHOD

Chop the shrimps and pound them well with the butter. Season with pepper and a little grated nutmeg, and add some lemon juice. Add the breadcrumbs and gradually blend in the fish stock. Stir until boiling and then rub through a wire sieve. Mix together the milk and egg yolks and add them to the slightly cooled soup. Stir over a slow flame until thickened but do not allow to boil. Correct seasoning and add more lemon juice if necessary. A few drops of red colouring may be used to give a pale pink colour. Stir in the cream at the last moment.

SHRIMP CHEESE BISQUE

INGREDIENTS: 4–6 portions

This is an American recipe.

1½ oz. butter
½ oz. flour
1½ pts milk
¼ lb. processed cheese cut into small dice
1 tin shrimps finely chopped

¼ teasp. Worcester sauce
1 dessertsp. chopped onion
2 tablesps. chopped green peppers
½ teasp. salt
Pepper

METHOD

Melt the fat and add pepper and onions. Cook over a low heat until tender but not brown. Blend in the flour and then add all the remaining ingredients. Stir until the cheese melts and the soup is hot but do not allow to boil.

TOMATO SOUP

INGREDIENTS: 5–7 portions

2 lb. fresh tomatoes or tinned tomatoes
1 carrot
1 small onion
1 stick celery
2 oz. lean ham or bacon
Bouquet garni

Pepper and salt
1 oz. butter
1 oz. flour or cornflour
1 teasp. sugar
1½ pts stock
⅛ pt cream
⅛ pt milk

METHOD

Slice the tomatoes into a stewpan and add the butter, ham, and chopped onion. Cook slowly with the lid on for 10 minutes, shaking the pan at intervals. Add the stock and finely cut carrot and celery. Bring to the boil, season, and lower the heat and simmer for 1 hour. Rub through a nylon sieve and return to the pan. Blend the cornflour with milk and stir this into the soup. Stir until boiling and simmer for 3 minutes. Correct the seasoning and add sugar to taste. Stir in cream just before serving.

VEGETABLE SOUP (WHITE)

INGREDIENTS: 6–8 portions

4 oz. carrot	1 oz. flour
4 oz. turnip	1½ pts white or vegetable
1 onion or small leek	stock
1 stalk celery	½ pt milk
Bouquet garni	1–2 tablesps. cream
1 dessertsp. chopped parsley	Pepper and salt
1 oz. butter	

METHOD

Prepare the vegetables and cut into tiny dice or strips the size of a matchstick – remembering that they remain in the soup when it is served and must be of a suitable size to take from a spoon with ease. Melt the butter in the stewpan, add the vegetables, and cook gently with the lid on for 10 minutes, shaking the pan at intervals. Add the stock, seasoning, and bouquet garni and simmer gently until the vegetables are done (15–30 minutes according to size). Remove the bouquet garni. Blend the flour with milk and stir into the soup. Stir until boiling and simmer for three minutes. Correct the seasoning, stir in the chopped parsley, and serve.

VEGETABLE SOUP (BROWN)

INGREDIENTS: 4–6 portions

1 carrot	1½ teasps. cornflour
1 very small turnip	1 oz. dripping
1 small onion	1½ pts brown stock

1 stick of celery	Seasoning
1 small potato	Bouquet garni
Gravy browning	½ teasp. Bovril

METHOD

Prepare the vegetables and slice thinly. Melt the dripping in a stewpan and fry the vegetables until brown, stirring constantly to prevent the potatoes sticking to the pan. Add the stock, Bovril, seasoning, and bouquet garni. Bring to the boil and then simmer for 1½ hours. Rub through a sieve. Mix the cornflour with a little cold stock and add to the soup. Stir until boiling, correct the seasoning, add gravy browning if necessary, and serve.

WATERCRESS SOUP

Most recipes for watercress soup contain a large proportion of potato, but it is possible to make this soup from the following ingredients for 4 portions:

2 bunches of watercress	Salt and pepper
1 oz. butter	1 egg yolk
¾ oz. flour	Use a few watercress stalks
1 pt white stock	in place of a bouquet
¼ pt milk	garni

METHOD

Wash the watercress and reserve twelve leaves for garnishing. Dip these into boiling water, drain them, and set them on one side until required. Chop the leaves and cook gently for 5 minutes in the butter. Add the stock, seasoning, and a few stalks, and boil for 5 minutes. Rub through a sieve. Blend the flour with milk and stir into the soup. Stir until boiling and simmer for 3 minutes. Correct the seasoning, and allow to cool slightly and then stir in the slightly beaten egg yolk and reheat gently. Serve with the blanched watercress leaves floating on the surface. A thin slice of onion can be cooked in this soup if desired.

STOCK

BROWN STOCK

INGREDIENTS

2 qts water
1 lb. beef bones
2 medium carrots
2 medium onions with
  cloves inserted
2 oz. lean bacon trimmings
Small turnip
¼ lb. tomatoes, or

⅛ pt tomato purée (2½ oz.)
12 white peppercorns
½ leek
½ stick celery
Pinch of salt
Bouquet garni

METHOD

Chop the bones and put them into a heavy pan. Brown them in a hot oven or over a flame. Pour off any fat. Add water, bring to the boil, and skim.

Wash and prepare the vegetables. Dice the vegetables and fry them in hot fat until brown. Strain off the fat and add the vegetables to the stock pot. Add seasoning and a bouquet garni. Simmer steadily until the vegetables are tender, keeping a lid on the pot. Remove the vegetables and continue to simmer the stock for 4–5 hours. Strain through a cloth or a nylon sieve. Cool rapidly and keep in a cold place. Remove the layer of solidified fat from the top before using the stock.

Reboil the stock daily and cool quickly after boiling. Do not keep it for more than three days.

The bones can be used for a second boiling of stock which will, obviously, have less flavour than the first boiling.

If a brown colour is not necessary, stock can be made by

placing the bones in water without preliminary frying of bones or vegetables.

A better flavour is given if a quarter-pound of shredded shin of beef is added.

WHITE STOCK

Use veal and/or chicken bones in place of beef bones and follow the recipe for brown stock – but omit all frying.

HAM STOCK

This is the water in which bacon or ham has been boiled. It must be allowed to get cold so that the fat can be lifted from the top. It is also necessary to taste it, lest it is too salty to use undiluted.

Ham stock is used for pulse soups.

VEGETABLE STOCK

The water in which vegetables have been cooked is frequently used as vegetable stock. Special stock can be prepared by boiling mixed vegetables, salt, pepper, and a bouquet garni in water for an hour. Care is necessary to ensure that strong flavours, e.g. turnip, do not predominate.

CHAPTER 2

Fish

FISH can be cooked by practically every method of cookery, except that it is done so quickly that pressure cooking is unnecessary. Because fish cooks quickly, care should be taken to see that it is not overdone, or it becomes dry. Boiling is not a good method to use, since moving water tends to break small pieces off the fish. For this reason, poaching is generally used. The liquid used may be water, stock, court bouillon, or (in a few cases) milk and water. These liquids should be well seasoned and brought to the boil. The fish is put in at boiling-point and the heat is immediately reduced so that the fish poaches in liquid off the boil.

COURT BOUILLON is made by boiling one pint of water and adding one tablespoonful of wine vinegar, a quarter of an ounce of salt, three peppercorns, and (optionally) a bouquet garni. One small carrot, a slice of onion, and half a bay leaf are also added. Boil all the ingredients for 30 minutes and then leave to get cold. Reheat when required.

Turbot and brill are best cooked with only salt and lemon juice in the water and there are those who prefer a salmon poached without herbs or vegetables in the cooking liquor.

FISH STOCK is prepared by putting into a pan:

1 lb. of white fish bones or trimmings (avoid cod which is too oily)	6 white peppercorns
	Juice of one lemon
	Small bay leaf
1 oz. butter	Pinch of salt
2 oz. onion	1½ pts water
Bouquet garni	

Bring to the boil and then simmer not more than 20 minutes. Strain and use. A better flavour is given if the following method is used:

Chop and blanch the onions, and cook slowly in the butter until clear but not brown. Add the fish trimmings, peppercorns, bay leaf, bouquet garni, and lemon juice and cover with greased paper and a lid. Cook very slowly indeed until all the essence has been extracted from the fish bones and then barely cover with water and simmer for 20 minutes.

The excellent flavour of sauces served with fish in *haute cuisine* depends very largely upon a well-flavoured fish stock. The cook who fails to make stock of good quality will be disappointed in the flavour of the sauce made from it. White wine added to cooking liquids used for fish gives an excellent flavour, but it causes white fish to look grey in colour. The addition of a little lemon juice prevents this.

POACHED FISH

When poached fish is cooked it should be drained on a fish slice and then wrapped in a clean cloth and kept in a warm place for a few minutes to allow liquid to seep out and be absorbed by the cloth. If this is not done there will be an unpleasant pool of liquid on the serving dish. Some uncoated poached fish is served on a napkin to absorb any liquid escaping.

If a coating sauce is poured over fish, it is essential that the surface is dry or the sauce tends to slide off. Furthermore, liquid seeping from the fish rises through the sauce and cracks the surface of it.

STEAMED FISH

Steamed and poached fish can be tied in muslin before cooking to make handling and draining easy. Steamed fish can be hung in muslin in the top compartment of a steamer, but small, thin cuts are frequently steamed between two plates resting on a pan of boiling water. This fish, too, should be well drained before serving.

GRILLED FISH

Grilled fish can be brushed with oil and lemon juice and exposed to radiant heat, or it can be prepared in the same way and wrapped in aluminium foil. By the first means a dry and slightly brown surface results; by the second means a moist surface is obtained and natural juices which are trapped within the foil can be poured over the fish. Foil is a heat insulator, and consequently it lengthens the time required to cook a piece of fish.

FRIED FISH

Delicately flavoured fish is usually fried in shallow fat. The surface is generally coated first in beaten egg and then in white or toasted breadcrumbs. This gives a crisp surface and seals in most of the natural juices. If fish is merely dipped in seasoned flour before frying, it has a less attractive appearance, and juices escaping into the frying fat or oil cause splashing. Oil, clarified dripping, or butter are suitable fats.

Frying in a deep bath of fat is used for fish which is coated with egg and breadcrumbs or batter. Oil, cooking fat, or dripping are suitable fats. All fried fish should be thoroughly dried on absorbent paper and served on a paper dish mat.

BAKED FISH

Baked fish is cooked alone or with a variety of added ingredients. It may also be stuffed. It should be covered with a sheet of greased paper or with foil or cooked in a casserole with a lid to prevent surface drying. Do not use a lid if a crisp surface is desired.

GARNISHING

Cooked fish should be attractively garnished. Lemon juice is generally added during preparation but lemon quarters served with the fish add to the appearance of the dish and add additional juice. Lemon butterflies form an attractive garnish and parsley adds colour to a dish. Fried parsley is excellent with fried fish. In recipes where mushroom, tomato, or shrimps are used, selected ones can be used for garnishing.

SAUCES

Since many fish lack strong flavours they are frequently served with well-flavoured sauces, e.g. Sole au gratin or Turbot Bercy. Time spent in preparing these sauces will lift a commonplace dish on to another plane. Furthermore, a really savoury sauce can be used to enhance the cheaper but equally nutritious fishes such as cod and coley.

Many people serve fish only with parsley, egg, or anchovy sauce, but tomato and brown sauce are delicious with many fish dishes and fennel or mustard sauce is served with herring or mackerel. The more specialized sauces given in the following recipes afford a great variety.

Since most cooks are capable of cooking fish by frying or poaching, most of the following recipes have been selected to emphasize the ways in which simple additions to simply cooked fish will raise a commonplace dish into a very special category.

*

BAKED HADDOCK

INGREDIENTS

A *small haddock – about 1 lb.*
2 *oz. dripping or cooking fat*
Stuffing:
   1½ *oz. breadcrumbs*
   1 *teasp. chopped parsley*

Pinch of herbs
Seasoning
1 *oz. melted butter*
Egg and milk
Lemon and parsley

METHOD

Scrape the scales from the fish, remove the eyes, and clean inside. Wash and dry. Mix the ingredients for the stuffing, adding enough egg and milk to make sure it holds together but is not wet. Pack the stuffing into the body cavity and sew it up. Pass two skewers through the body to fix it into an 'S' shape, or break the bone between the eye sockets and push the tail through and secure it with a small skewer. Heat the dripping in a deep tin in a moderately hot oven (375°). Put the fish in the tin and baste it with hot dripping. Bake for 20 minutes, or for an extra 10 minutes a pound if it is a larger fish, basting two or three times. Serve on a hot dish with parsley and lemon garnish.

To test when the fish is done, insert a fine skewer or the point of a knife through the thickest part of the flesh at the shoulder. If the flesh is opaque and white right to the backbone, the fish is done.

Serve with anchovy or brown sauce.

BAKED STUFFED PLAICE

INGREDIENTS

1 plaice ¾–1 lb.	Salt and pepper
Melted butter or olive oil	Bread raspings
Lemon juice	Lemon and parsley

Stuffing: No. 1

As for baked haddock, **or**

Stuffing: No. 2

1½ oz. breadcrumbs	1 oz. melted butter
1 oz. chopped shrimps	Egg and milk
Pepper and salt	

METHOD

Tear the black skin off the plaice. Cut off the head, or leave it on and remove the eyes. Clean the body cavity, rubbing off any black skin with salt on the tip of the finger. Wash and dry. Season and sprinkle with lemon juice. Slit down the centre line of the fish and lift the fillets from the bone, leaving them attached to the sides of the fish. Pack the stuffing between the fillets and the bone and replace the fillets over it. Brush the surface with melted butter, margarine, or oil, and sprinkle with bread raspings. Place in a greased baking tin or earthenware dish, cover with greased paper and bake at 375° until flesh is just cooked. Garnish with lemon and parsley. If shrimp stuffing is used, reserve two or three shrimps for garnishing. Serve with parsley, anchovy, or shrimp sauce.

BRANDADE OF COD

INGREDIENTS

1 lb. salt cod   Pepper
Olive oil   Chopped parsley
1 crushed clove garlic

METHOD

Wash the cod several times in fresh water and then soak for 24 hours in cold water. Drain the fish and put it in a pan with water just enough to cover it. Bring to the boil, remove from the heat, and leave to stand in the water for 15 minutes. Drain it and remove the flesh from the bones. Put the flesh in a thick pan and add two tablespoons of oil, working it well with a wooden spoon. As it starts to thicken add more oil and then a little of the cooking stock and then more oil, continuing until the whole is really smooth and creamy. Stir vigorously all the time and add the oil drop by drop.

There are advocates of milk in place of fish stock; you can choose which you prefer. In any case, less than a quarter of a pint of either is required, but the main liquid used should be oil (about half a pint).

A pinch of pepper and a crushed clove of garlic and chopped parsley are stirred in when cooking is complete. If raw garlic is displeasing, this vegetable can be put in the pan when the fish is boiled and removed before oil is added. Lemon juice can be added if desired.

Care is necessary to prevent the oil separating out – this will happen if the mixture is too hot, if stirring is interrupted, or if the oil is added too quickly.

BRILL NIÇOISE

A fish with firm flesh is delicious cooked this way. From mullet to halibut there is a wide range of price, but the result is uniformly pleasing.

INGREDIENTS

1 lb. brill	1 clove garlic
1 tablesp. olive oil	1 tablesp. parsley
2 shallots	6 black olives
3 oz. mushrooms	2 tablesps. dry white wine

METHOD

Wash and dry the fish and brush with oil. Grill on each side for 2 minutes. Put the remaining oil in a small pan, chop the rest of the ingredients very finely, and cook slowly in the oil with a lid on the pan. Shake at intervals until the vegetables are cooked. Grease an earthenware dish and lay the cooked vegetables and wine in the bottom with the fish resting on the vegetables. Cover with greased paper and bake until done in an oven at 400°. This will take about 15 minutes. This dish is excellent served cold.

DEVILLED LOBSTER

It is said that the kindest way to cook a lobster is to put it
into lukewarm salted water and heat fairly gently to boiling-
point. It should be boiled for 20-30 minutes according to its
size and allowed to cool in the cooking liquor.

To prepare lobster, insert the point of a sharp chef's knife
in the centre of the head and lay the blade along the length
of the tail. Make one quick cut to sever the tail into two
equal portions. Turn the fish round, put the point of the
knife in the centre position again and cut the head in two.
Crack the large claws and remove all the meat. Remove the
intestine (a green line running the length of the fish) and
stomach and serve the rest. The meat is delectable served
cold with salad and tartare sauce, but there are many ways of
reheating lobster. One of them is as devilled lobster.

INGREDIENTS

1 boiled lobster – medium size	1½ oz. butter
	2 tablesps. cream
3 tablesps. white bread-crumbs	Cayenne pepper
	Lemon and parsley

METHOD

Chop the claw and tail meat. Melt the fat and pour on to
the lobster. Add most of the crumbs, the cream, and the
cayenne pepper and season with salt. Polish the lobster shells
with oil and press the meat mixture lightly into them. Cover
with the remaining crumbs and small pats of butter. Bake
for 15 minutes at the top of a moderately hot oven (375°)
and serve garnished with parsley and lemon sections.

DRESSED CRAB

Choose a crab which is heavy for its size and with a clean smooth shell.

Lay the crab on its back, hold the shell firmly with one hand and the body (to which the claws are attached) in the other hand, and pull apart. Take the shell apart and with a spoon remove the stomach bag which lies just below the head, discard this. Carefully scrape all the meat from the shell into a basin and reserve it. Break away the shell as far as the groove near the outer rim. Wash and dry the shell and polish it with oil. Add a tablespoonful or so of fresh breadcrumbs to the brown meat, season with salt, pepper, and vinegar, or with a little Worcestershire sauce. Mix in some chopped parsley and pack this mixture into the sides of the prepared shell, leaving a space in the middle.

Take the body and remove from it the 'dead man's fingers' or gills, which are inedible, and discard these. Crack the claws and the body with nutcrackers or a weight and take out all the white meat from the claws and the body. Flake this fish with a fork, season with salt, cayenne pepper, and add a little cream. Pile it at the centre of the shell.

Decorate the crab with a little chopped parsley and the yolk and white of hard-boiled egg sieved separately.

Chop the joints off the small claws and push the tip of one claw into the open end of another, thus forming a ring. Place the crab on a dish within this ring so that it balances steadily. Garnish with selected pieces of salad vegetables.

SCALLOPS

Remove the scallops from their shells and trim off their beards and black parts. Wash well.

They can now be cooked in many ways; two of the most popular are stewed and fried.

STEWED SCALLOPS

Blanch the scallops in boiling water and refresh in cold. Cut each one into three or four pieces. Have a small pan containing equal quantities of white wine and fish stock with a little lemon juice added. Boil this to reduce the volume by a half and to leave enough in the pan barely to cover the fish. Drop the fish in and simmer gently until cooked (20–30 minutes). Mix together in a basin equal quantities of butter or margarine and flour, one ounce of each to three-quarter pint of stock. Drop this into the stewpan, stirring until the sauce is thickened. Adjust the seasoning and serve in a hot dish with lemon and parsley as a garnish.

Various additions to this recipe are possible. For instance, a little shallot can be chopped finely and cooked till clear in a small amount of fat and the stock and scallops can be put in the same pan. Chopped mushrooms or parsley used separately or together will alter the flavour of the stew.

FRIED SCALLOPS

Cut the scallops as for stewing and dip each piece in egg seasoned with pepper and salt and then into breadcrumbs. Fry in hot fat until golden brown, drain on kitchen paper, and serve with lemon quarters and fried parsley.

FISH AU VIN BLANC

This is delectable and, although extravagant, will probably find its way into your list of special dishes. Make a court bouillon using a glass of white wine to a pint of water instead of the wine vinegar given in an earlier recipe. When it has boiled for 20 minutes place in it a sole or turbot or a freshwater fish and poach gently until done (probably about 20 minutes).

The sauce must be ready to serve at the same moment as the fish. It is prepared from the following ingredients:

¼ pt white wine	⅛ pt court bouillon
8 very small shallots chopped finely	6 oz. butter

METHOD

Put the shallots in a pan with the wine and court bouillon and let it boil until only about two tablespoons remain. Put this in the top of a double saucepan or in a basin standing over a pan of hot water. Soften the butter and add a little at a time to the liquid until it is all used up, whisking the whole time so that a foamy sauce is produced. Be careful not to allow it to get too hot or the butter will become oil and the sauce will be ruined. Taste for seasoning before serving.

FISH BONNE FEMME

INGREDIENTS

About 2 lb. of any filleted white fish, salmon, or salmon trout	your own taste) 3–4 oz. butter
Finely chopped shallots, finely chopped parsley, sliced mushrooms (to	Pepper, salt, and lemon juice ½ pt fish stock and ⅛ pt white wine, or ¼ pt stock and ¼ pt wine

The shallot must be very finely chopped or it will not be completely cooked when it is served.

METHOD

Grease a fireproof dish and sprinkle with shallots, parsley, and very thinly sliced mushroom. Lay on this the washed and seasoned fillets of fish, and cover them with the remaining vegetables. Sprinkle with lemon juice. Add white wine and fish stock to come half-way up the fish. Lay a sheet of greased paper on top and bake in a fairly hot oven (400°) until tender. Thin fillets will require only 7–8 minutes, thicker cuts take longer.

Remove the fish to a hot serving dish and keep in a warm place. Pour the cooking liquor into a small pan and boil until the volume is reduced by half. From now on you can finish the dish in the classic manner or take an easy way out. Classically, butter is worked in a little at a time (with the pan drawn to the side of the stove) with vigorous stirring. When the sauce thickens, correct the seasoning and pour it over the fish and brown at once under a hot grill. This is really a variant of Hollandaise sauce.

It is cheaper and easier to make a little sauce with fat, flour, and fish stock and to pour into this the reduced cooking liquor. Once again, brown under the grill. A little lemon juice and butter or cream added to this sauce just before serving will improve it.

FISH MAYONNAISE

Salmon, salmon trout, turbot, or other firm fish may be used.

INGREDIENTS

Mayonnaise   *Aspic jelly*

To decorate, take a selection from the following :

1 *leaf of leek blanched in*   *A little tomato flesh, or*
  boiling water   *tinned red pepper, or*
Watercress leaves blanched   *the red outside of a radish*
  in boiling water   *Truffle*
Hard-boiled egg   *Cucumber skin*

METHOD

Cook the fish in a court bouillon and remove the skin. Replace it in the cooking liquor and leave until cold. Dry well on a clean cloth, place on a wire rack and cool for a few minutes in a refrigerator.

In the meantime take some aspic crystals and dissolve them in the recommended amount of water and leave to get cold. When the jelly is cold but not set, add it to twice its own volume of mayonnaise and stir the two together gently until they are on the point of setting. If they are whisked together there will be air bubbles in the mixture and these will spoil the surface of the mayonnaise. The basin containing the mayonnaise mixture can stand on ice so long as the contents are stirred all the time, but if stirring is interrupted the edges will have set on the basin. The mixture of one part double-strength aspic and two parts mayonnaise is called mayonnaise collée, and is used for coating meat or fish.

Place the rack of fish over a large plate and spoon the mayonnaise mixture smoothly over it when it is on the point of setting. This should set at once and coat the fish perfectly. Leave in a cold place for 5 minutes to become firm, then take a little cold aspic jelly and dip each piece of the decoration into it in turn and then place into position on top of the fish, using a sewing needle to impale the pieces. Unless each piece is dipped into aspic it will not set on to the mayonnaise and will then wash off when the surface is glazed.

The decoration used depends on individual artistic skill. A little flower-pot of radish skin with a stem of leek and drooping leaves of leek or of watercress can be surmounted by a flower with petals of tinned red pepper or hard-boiled egg white. A little truffle improves a green and white decoration, but is so expensive that thin slivers of pickled walnut dried on a cloth can be used instead. An artist may produce a bird with a long sweeping tail composed of halved slices of radish as thin as tissue paper. The red skin outlines each of the feathers on the wing and tail.

When the decoration is complete it is left in a cold place to set on the surface of the fish and then the rest of the aspic jelly at setting point is spooned quickly over the whole surface. In a few moments this sets to give a brilliant gloss to the surface.

Cut the fish off the wire tray and serve on a large dish with a few heart leaves of lettuce, slices of cucumber, and pieces of tomato as a garnish.

FISH MEUNIÈRE

Dabs are pleasant cooked this way. Make two deep cuts in an 'X' shape in the thickest part of the flesh on both sides of the fish, and then clean, wash, and dry it. Dip in seasoned flour immediately before frying and fry on one side until golden brown in a pan containing a shallow layer of foaming butter. Turn and fry on the other side. Fry one soft roe for every dab and serve with a roe on top of each fish and chopped parsley as a garnish. Put wedges of lemon at the end of the dish. Heat a little extra butter in the pan until it is nut-brown, and pour it over the fish.

FILLETS MEUNIÈRES

Fillets of fish can be cooked the same way and dished up overlapping each other. While the fish is being prepared, cut some tomatoes and mushrooms into thick, oblique slices, brush with melted fat, and cook under the grill. Lay alternate slices of mushroom and tomato down the centre of each fillet and sprinkle the whole with chopped parsley. Add more butter (margarine will not do) to the frying-pan and heat until the fat is nut-brown, pour this over the fish, and serve at once.

FISH MORNAY

Mornay sauce is cheese sauce and is prepared by melting one ounce of margarine or butter in a small pan and working into it one ounce of flour and then gradually stirring in half a pint of milk. Stir until boiling, season with salt and a little cayenne pepper, and then (not before or your sauce will be stringy) stir in two ounces of grated cheese. To improve it, a little cream or the yolk of an egg can be worked in when it has cooled slightly and more butter can also be added.

To serve fish Mornay, cook the fish, by poaching, baking, or grilling it, and then dry it well in a cloth so that liquid does not ooze out of it and crack the surface of the sauce. Lay the fish on a hot serving dish and mask it with mornay sauce. A little grated cheese can be sprinkled over the surface and then browned under a hot grill.

If different garnishes are used the dish takes a different name: e.g. small bundles of cooked asparagus tips or of French beans can be laid at each end of the dish and a slice of truffle on top. It then becomes GRAND DUC.

If the cooked fish is placed on the serving dish and a slice of cooked lobster is placed on each piece of fish and a slice of truffle on the lobster and then mornay sauce is poured over, the dish is FISH WALESKI.

FISH AMBASSADEUR is prepared by putting a little mornay sauce and mushroom purée on each fish fillet before it is cooked and folding the fillet in two, to enclose the stuffing. More mushroom purée is worked into the remaining mornay sauce before coating the cooked fish with it.

FISH FLORENTINE is always served with spinach. In this case, the fillets of fish are baked in the oven with a little fish stock round them and a piece of paper on top. Spinach is boiled for 7 minutes and then drained well and pressed free from moisture in a cloth or on a sieve. It is then returned to the hot pan and a little butter is stirred into it as well as salt and pepper. The spinach is laid all over the centre of the serving dish and the cooked fillets are placed on top. The fish stock from the baking dish is boiled down to reduce its volume and is stirred into the mornay sauce before coating the fish with it. Cheese is sprinkled on top of the surface and the dish is browned under the grill.

FISH OMELET

Make an omelet in the usual way and, when it is ready to serve, spread the fish mixture on the centre and fold both sides of the omelet over it.

Any left-over cooked fish, white or smoked, is suitable for this purpose. It should be flaked up and all skin and bone removed. Place it in a pan and add either a little white sauce or one or two tablespoons of cream or some butter. Heat through and season well and keep hot until required. Shrimps, prawns, or flaked lobster flesh can be used.

FISH SALAD WITH FENNEL

Fennel is excellent with fish and can be used to flavour fish sauces, or can be incorporated in a dish as in this recipe.

Wash a raw fennel root and shred three to four tablespoons as finely as tobacco. Use it in the following salad:

INGREDIENTS

1 lb. cooked fish broken into flakes
½ lettuce shredded finely
3–4 tablesps. fennel shredded finely

Mayonnaise
Hard-boiled egg
Pepper and salt

METHOD

Put the fish in a large bowl and add sufficient lettuce to suit your taste, the shredded fennel, and seasoning. Mix together and pile in a glass bowl. Coat with mayonnaise and garnish with hard-boiled egg and fennel sprays.

The fish and the vegetables can be bound together with a little mayonnaise before putting them into the serving dish.

When it is in season, a little shredded celery can be used instead of or as well as fennel. Some other vegetables and fruits can replace celery, for example chicory or avocado pear. The pear will darken if it is not placed in lemon juice and water for a few moments before draining it and adding it to the salad. Tomato can also be used, but it should be skinned and the seeds should be removed before the flesh is sliced. If salmon is used to make the salad, there should be a garnish of cucumber.

FISH SALAD IN ASPIC

INGREDIENTS

1 lb. flaked fish (lobster meat is excellent for this)	Tomato
	Cucumber
1 pt aspic jelly	Cooked peas
2 hard-boiled eggs	Cooked broad beans
1 lettuce	Diced, cooked carrots

METHOD

Skin the tomatoes, remove the seeds, and cut the flesh into dice. Peel the cucumber and slice it thinly. Take a ring mould and pour into it a thin layer of aspic jelly and leave to set. Decorate this with sliced cucumber and hard-boiled egg. Pour a very thin layer of cold aspic over the garnish and leave to set. Arrange the peas, beans, and carrots in the mould and then the fish and tomatoes. Wait until the aspic is quite cold and fill the mould with it. Leave until set and then dip quickly into hot water and turn on to a serving dish. Garnish with lettuce leaves, cucumber slices, and wedges of tomato.

FRIED WHITEBAIT

Do not wash whitebait, but remove any foreign bodies from them and dip in well-seasoned flour. The easiest way to do this is to put the flour in a paper bag, add the fish, and shake well. Tip on to a sieve to remove excess flour. Heat a bath of fat until a very faint haze appears, place the fish in a frying basket and lower them into the fat. Leave until they are beginning to colour. Lift the frying basket from the fat bath and raise the heat under the fat until a haze again rises. Lower the fish a second time and cook until golden brown. By frying twice, the whitebait are less greasy than if they remain in the fat until they are done. Drain well on absorbent paper and serve with quarters of lemon and cayenne pepper.

The traditional accompaniment is thinly sliced brown bread and butter. This can be replaced by a small helping of starch-reduced rolls.

LOBSTER PARISIENNE

INGREDIENTS

1 cooked lobster
Mayonnaise
Aspic jelly
1 lettuce

Cooked diced carrot, turnip,
    and French beans, and
    cooked peas
1 tomato
Parsley

METHOD

Cook the lobster (see Devilled Lobster, page 57). Split in two and clean. Remove the claws and crack carefully to keep the pink flesh from the tip of the large claws intact. Break the remaining claw meat into small pieces and put in a bowl with some cooked peas and some diced cooked carrots, turnips, and beans. Mix in a little mayonnaise. Remove the tail meat from the lobster shells and polish the shells with oil. Lay the vegetable salad in the tail shells. Slice the tail meat diagonally into fairly thick pieces and lay these over the vegetable salad, having the curved side uppermost. Lay the claw flesh in the head shells. Coat with mayonnaise collée (see Mayonnaise of Fish, page 61). Decorate with hard-boiled egg or vegetables and glaze with aspic. Serve on a dish mat with a garnish of parsley.

PLAICE DUGLÉRÉ

INGREDIENTS

1 lb. plaice, whole or in fillets	Chopped parsley
	Bouquet garni
2 teasps. finely chopped onion	½–¾ pt fish stock
	½ oz. flour
½ lb. skinned and diced tomatoes, free from seeds	1 oz. butter

METHOD

Remove the dark skin from the plaice. Grease a shallow pan and place the cleaned fish in it. Sprinkle a little chopped onion, some parsley, and the tomato flesh over the fish. Add the bouquet garni and barely cover with stock. Cover with a lid, bring to the boil, and then poach gently for 10–25 minutes, depending on the thickness of the fish. Drain the fish on a clean cloth and lift on to a serving dish and keep warm. Reduce the stock to half its volume. Mix the flour and butter together and add them to the stock, stirring until thickened and boiling. Remove the bouquet garni and pour the sauce (still containing onion, tomato, and parsley) over the fish. Sprinkle with chopped parsley.

If the onion is not very finely chopped it may not cook sufficiently while the fish is cooking.

The quantity of flour and butter required for thickening will vary with the amount of stock used. It is safer not to add it all at once in case the whole quantity is not required.

Other fish may also be cooked in this way.

PLAICE SUCHET

Other fish can be used instead of plaice. Fillets are best for this dish and the dark skin should be removed from them.

INGREDIENTS

1 lb. fillets of plaice
Up to ½ or ¾ pt fish stock (see p. 49)
½ pt white sauce made with:
  1¼ oz. butter
  1¼ oz. flour
  ¼ pt fish stock
  ¼ pt milk

Chopped parsley
1 tablesp. each of carrot, celery, onion, and leek, all cut into strips the size of a matchstick and boiled in salted water until tender. This takes only a few minutes

METHOD

Grease a baking dish and lay in it the washed and seasoned fillets of fish. Sprinkle over the top the julienne of cooked vegetables. Add a little fish stock which must not cover the fish. Cover with greased paper and cook in a moderate oven (350°) until done. This takes about 10 minutes. Lift the fillets on to a serving dish, heap the vegetables on top of them, and keep hot. Bring the white sauce to the boil and strain enough cooking liquor into it to give a coating consistency. Coat the fish and sprinkle with chopped parsley.

Some cooks reserve the julienne and sprinkle it on top of the coating sauce instead of placing it on the fillets while they are cooking. If this is done the appearance is improved by the addition of a few fine shreds of truffle or pickled walnut.

PRAWNS: CURRIED

Pacific prawns or the smaller everyday variety are equally good for curry. Other shellfish can be used instead. The curry sauce is prepared first and the cooked fish is only warmed in the sauce just before serving. If white fish is used instead of shellfish it should be free from skin and bone and cut into fairly large pieces. These are placed, raw, into the curry sauce and heated only long enough to cook them. If they are overcooked they break apart when served.

SAUCE INGREDIENTS

4 oz. onions or shallots
1 clove garlic
4 oz. cooking apple
½ pt water or fish stock
1 tablesp. desiccated coconut
1 tablesp. curry powder (1 dessertsp. only if a mild curry is required)

1 teasp. curry-paste
1 teasp. black treacle
2 oz. butter or margarine
Lemon juice
4 oz. tomatoes
Seasoning
½ oz. rice flour
Parsley

Accompaniments to curry – boiled rice, lemon slices.

METHOD

Peel and chop finely the garlic, onion, and apple. Fry them in butter until they are clear but not brown, stir in the curry powder and paste and fry a little longer. Add the water or stock, coconut, treacle, and tomato flesh. Add seasoning and simmer 40 minutes with a lid on the pan. Blend the rice flour with a little cold stock, stir this into the sauce and stir until boiling. Simmer for 3–5 minutes. Add a little lemon juice and place the fish into the sauce with a spoon. Heat for a short time. Serve with lemon slices and plain boiled rice.

Although desiccated coconut is frequently served in the curry sauce there are many who prefer to infuse it for half an hour in a boiling stock and then to strain off the nut and discard it. Freshly grated coconut, of course, gives a far better flavour than the dried.

SALMON

Salmon and salmon trout can be cooked similarly. The latter has a more delicate flavour than salmon.

There are many ways of cooking and serving these fish but the most usual are poaching and grilling. The fish may be poached in court bouillon, but many prefer to use salted water with lemon juice so that no additional flavour is superimposed on the very distinctive and delicate flavour of the fish itself. The length of time required for cooking varies with the thickness of the fish; thin tail pieces or cutlets poach in about 7 minutes per pound, larger or whole fish require 8 minutes per pound. Overcooking should be avoided. A pan on top of the stove or a deep baking dish inside a slow oven (300°–325°) are equally satisfactory for this method of cooking. A salmon kettle is obtainable for use on a hotplate. This is a long, narrow container with a lid, which will accommodate the length of the whole fish. Large oval casseroles often accommodate salmon without difficulty.

It is usual to strip the skin off before serving the cooked fish and to decorate the flesh with overlapping slices of cucumber and, if liked, hard-boiled eggs. A parsley and lemon garnish can also be used.

GRILLED SALMON

Steaks are frequently used for this purpose and should be brushed with lemon juice and then oil. They are seared on both sides under a hot grill and then the heat is lowered to complete cooking. It is necessary to turn the fish every 2 minutes to ensure that it is cooked equally and not dried on one side. Palette knives, fish slices, or other blunt utensils should be used to turn the fish. Grilled food should never be pierced with a knife or fork to turn it. Garnish as for poached salmon. Hot salmon is served with Hollandaise or other suitable piquant sauce, or with maître d'hôtel butter, and cold salmon is usually served with tartare sauce or one of a variety of sauces based on mayonnaise. Both are accompanied by cucumber salad.

Pickled Salmon

Left-over salmon can be treated in this way after the bones have been removed. The flesh should be laid in a deep dish and covered with the pickling liquid and left to stand in it for 12 hours.

PICKLE INGREDIENTS

Equal quantities of vinegar and liquid in which the fish was cooked.

To every pint of liquid add:

¼ oz. peppercorns	A sprig of lemon
½ teasp. salt	Thyme
A bay leaf	¼ oz. of whole allspice

Boil all these together for 10 minutes (it is wise to tie the spices and herbs in a piece of muslin) and allow them to get cold. When cold, pour them over the salmon and leave for at least 12 hours, but the fish will keep in this pickle for several days.

Salmon Mousse

This is delicious made with fresh salmon, but also very good with tinned salmon.

INGREDIENTS

½ lb. cooked salmon rubbed
   through a nylon sieve or
   creamed in an electric
   blender

½ pt mayonnaise
½ pt cream for whipping
1 gill fish stock
A good ½ oz. gelatine

TO DECORATE:

Aspic jelly and small pieces of cucumber, tomato, truffle,
hard-boiled egg, or watercress.

METHOD

Take several small metal dariole moulds or a one and a half
pint metal mould and line the base with a very thin layer
of aspic jelly. Leave this to set. Blanch thin strips of cucumber skin and some watercress leaves and arrange a design
from these and other suitable foods in the aspic. Carefully
put a very thin layer of cold aspic over the decoration and
leave it to set. Make the mousse as follows: Soak the gelatine for a few minutes in half the cold fish stock and then
place the basin containing it in a pan of boiling water
until the gelatine has dissolved. Beat the cream slightly
until it is a soft foam. Stir the mayonnaise into the salmon and carefully fold the whipped cream into this mixture, using a metal tablespoon. Fold in half the fish stock.
Add the dissolved gelatine cooled to a little more than
blood heat and fold this in quickly and carefully. Pour the
mixture into the decorated mould and leave to set. Lower
the mould into a bowl of hot water and remove at once –
this loosens the mousse which can then be turned into a
serving dish and garnished with cucumber slices and salad
vegetables.

Home-made mayonnaise prepared from egg yolks, oil, and
vinegar is the best to use for this recipe. If commercial
mayonnaise has to be used it imparts a strong flavour to

the mousse and it is wise to use only quarter of a pint and to replace the other quarter pint with cream.

SCAMPI

When scampi appeared on the market a few years ago they became a fashion. Our own Dublin Bay prawns which had been with us for years are virtually the same. Scampi differ in that they hail from the Mediterranean. When caught in France they are called *langoustines*. They are most popular when fried.

METHOD

Dip each prawn into beaten seasoned egg and then into breadcrumbs. Lower into a bath of deep fat from which a very faint haze is rising and fry until golden brown. This does not take long and the fish should not be overcooked or they will be dry. When properly done, scampi are juicy and succulent. Drain on paper and serve on a dish paper with lemon slices and fresh parsley as a garnish. Tartare or Hollandaise sauce can accompany fried scampi.

SCALLOPED FISH

INGREDIENTS

1 lb. of any cooked fish
flaked and freed from skin
or bone
¾ oz. butter
½ oz. flour
¼ pt milk

½–1 teasp. anchovy essence
¼ teasp. made mustard
Cayenne pepper
Breadcrumbs
Lemon and parsley

METHOD

Make a sauce with the butter, flour, and milk, stir until boiling, and simmer for 2–3 minutes. Season with pepper, mustard, and anchovy essence. Add salt if required. Stir in the flaked fish. Grease some scallop shells and fill with the fish mixture, sprinkle crumbs over the surface of each and dot with margarine or butter. Brown under a quick grill. Garnish with lemon and parsley.

SKATE AND BROWN BUTTER

The only part of skate which is eaten is the fins or 'wings'. These are frequently large enough for one to serve three people. To prepare them, wash in clean water and scrub well with a brush. Rinse and dry. Cut off the fringe of gristle from the edge and then divide into strips, each of which represents one portion. The prepared pieces can be cooked in a court bouillon for 20–30 minutes and then drained well on a clean cloth or absorbent paper. The skin should be removed from both sides and the fish put into a serving dish. Browned butter, caper sauce, or parsley sauce can accompany skate.

Browned butter is prepared as follows and poured over the cooked fish:

INGREDIENTS

2 oz. butter   2 teasps. chopped parsley
2 teasps. vinegar

METHOD

Heat the butter in a small pan until it is nut-brown. Remove the pan from the flame and stir in the vinegar and parsley. Pour over the fish and garnish with sprigs of parsley.

SKATE FRIED IN BUTTER

It is usual to marinate skate 'wings' for at least 1½ hours in equal parts of vinegar and water to which has been added pepper and salt, a sliced onion, some parsley, and the juice

of half a lemon. Drain and dry the fish. Dip the pieces in egg
and then breadcrumbs and fry in butter, or coat with batter
and fry in deep fat until a golden brown colour. Drain on
paper. Serve very hot on a dish paper with lemon quarters
as a garnish. Sauce need not accompany fried skate, but a
Tartare sauce is generally acceptable or nut-brown butter
can be served.

SOLE AU GRATIN

INGREDIENTS

2 sole (approximately 1 lb.)   *Chopped parsley*
  (Plaice can be used   *Browned breadcrumbs*
  instead)   *Salt and pepper*
1 tablesp. white wine   *Lemon slices and parsley*
Lemon juice   *Italian sauce (see Sauces,*
2 oz. mushrooms   *Chapter 7)*

METHOD

Wash the sole and tear the skin off both sides. Remove the
head and fins. Cut several incisions across the flesh of one
side of the fish and lay it in a greased baking dish with the
cut side uppermost. Season with pepper and salt. Add the
white wine and a few drops of lemon juice. Skin and slice
the mushrooms and cook in a covered pan for 3 minutes with
a quarter ounce butter, a few drops of lemon juice, salt and
pepper. Strain and reserve the mushrooms. Add the liquor
to the fish. Sprinkle chopped parsley over the fish and lay
a row of sliced, cooked mushrooms down the centre. Cover
with Italian sauce and sprinkle with browned breadcrumbs.
Cover with greased paper and bake in a moderate oven
(375°) for 20–30 minutes according to the thickness of the
fish. Garnish with parsley and lemon slices.

SOLE ROUENNAISE

INGREDIENTS

4 fillets of sole	Stuffing made from:
Lemon juice	½ oz. butter
Pepper and salt	½ oz. flour
½ pt white coating sauce	⅛ pt milk
Lemon and parsley	1½–2 oz. chopped shrimps

METHOD

Skin the fillets, wash and dry them, and lay each on a board with the skinned side uppermost. Sprinkle with lemon juice and seasoning. Melt the butter in a pan, add the flour, and fry until of a sandy texture. Stir in the milk and boil for 2 minutes. Add the chopped shrimps and season well. Divide into four portions and place one portion on the centre of each fillet. Fold both ends of the fillet over the stuffing and invert each fillet. Place in a greased baking dish and cover with greased paper. Bake until done (about 10 minutes) in an oven at 375°. Lift on to a clean cloth and dry well. Place on the serving dish and pour a coating of Béchamel or Velouté sauce over the fillets, garnish with lemon and parsley.

A few shrimps can also be used to garnish this dish.

ROES

SOFT ROES

Soft roes are often dipped in seasoned flour, fried in shallow fat, and served on hot buttered toast. They may, however, be baked.

BAKED ROES

INGREDIENTS

2–3 tomatoes
Grated lemon zest and 1
  teasp. juice
Chopped parsley

½ lb. soft roes
Salt and pepper
2 tablesps. white wine
Breadcrumbs

METHOD

Squeeze the juice from a slice of onion, either in a garlic press or in muslin. Skin the tomatoes, remove the seeds, and chop the flesh coarsely. Grease a baking dish and lay the washed, seasoned roes in it. Mix the tomato, onion juice, parsley, lemon zest and juice together and spread over the roes. Pour the white wine over the top. Cover with greased paper and bake in a moderate oven (375°) for 10–15 minutes.

CREAMED ROES

INGREDIENTS

½ lb. soft roes
¼ pt milk
½ oz. butter
½ oz. flour

Pepper and salt
Grated lemon zest (optional)
Parsley and lemon quarters

METHOD

Wash the roes and simmer in milk for 5 minutes. Mash well or rub through a nylon sieve. Melt the butter in a pan, add the flour and fry until of a sandy texture. Work in milk and then the mashed roes, bring to the boil and season well. Add lemon zest if required. Serve on hot buttered toast with parsley sprigs and lemon quarters to garnish.

SOUSED MACKEREL OR HERRING

INGREDIENTS

3 mackerel or herring
1 teasp. chopped onion
6 peppercorns
Vinegar and water in equal
    proportions

Either 1 bay leaf or
3 cloves or
dill seeds tied in muslin or
sprays of fresh dill

METHOD

Slit the fish and remove the backbone and all large bones.
Wash and dry. Lay a little chopped onion on each fish and
roll up from the head end. Secure with a wooden cocktail
stick or a skewer made from a sharpened match or tie with
cotton. Lay in a baking dish and barely cover with vinegar
and water. Add herbs to taste. The flavour of the fish can
be completely different according to the choice of herbs.
Cover with a lid and bake in a very slow oven (300°–325°)
for 40–45 minutes. Remove the herbs. Serve hot or cold.
If served cold, allow to cool in the cooking liquid.

SOUSED (COOKED) RIVER TROUT

This is excellent. If, however, you wish to economize, try
this recipe with herring in place of trout.

INGREDIENTS

3 trout
Salt and pepper and flour
Olive oil to fry the trout
1 thinly sliced onion or 2
    shallots
A crushed clove of garlic
1 sage leaf
1 small bay leaf

Sprig of rosemary
3 peppercorns
1 chilli
1 dessertsp. olive oil
2 tablesps. red wine vinegar
    or red wine
4 tablesps. water
Parsley and lemon quarters

METHOD

Clean, wash, and dry the trout and dip in flour seasoned with salt and pepper. Fry carefully on both sides in olive oil. Place into a dish which only just holds them. Fry onion or shallots in a dessertspoonful of olive oil until quite tender but not brown. Add all the other ingredients and pour this marinade over the fish. Leave for 12 hours and then turn them and leave another 12 hours. Remove the garlic, chilli, and herbs and serve with the marinade. Garnish with parsley and lemon quarters.

STUFFED HALIBUT (OR OTHER FLAT FISH)

Flat fish can be boned before stuffing, which makes them more pleasant to eat and easier to serve. Turbot, halibut, John Dory, brill, and large soles or plaice can be prepared this way.

Lay the fish on the edge of the table and hold the fins extended in one hand. Cut off with a sharp knife, using a sawing motion and working from tail to head. Lay the fish on the table, dark skin uppermost, and slit down the natural line in the centre which marks the position of the backbone. Lift the fillets with a sharp knife to within half an inch of the sides of the fish, but do not remove them completely. Then insert the point of a knife for a distance of one to one and a half inches beneath the backbone and slide the blade to within half an inch of the side of the fish on either side of the backbone. Break this short length of backbone from the rest by a sharp movement upwards to snap the bone at the centre. It is now attached to the fish only by the half-inch length which has not been severed from the sides of the fins. Take a strong pair of scissors and cut through the bone half an inch from the side of the fish and remove this part of the backbone. Repeat the process until the whole skeleton is removed. It is only possible to do a short length at a time or the flesh will be perforated.

If sole is being boned, tear off the dark skin before cutting the flesh.

Wash and dry the fish and sprinkle both sides with lemon juice, pepper, and salt. Pack the centre with stuffing and lay the whole fish (dark side downwards) in a large greased baking dish. Brush the surface with oil or melted butter, sprinkle with lemon juice and cover with greased paper. Bake in a moderate oven (375°) until tender. Take a knife and flick along both sides of the fish from head to tail in order to remove the short length of bone left in it. Lift the now boneless fish on to a serving dish and garnish appropriately. Serve coated with sauce or pass a pouring sauce separately.

One suitable filling for a halibut or chicken turbot weighing about four pounds is made from the following:

1 lb. whiting	Lemon juice
Pepper and salt	¼–½ pt cream

METHOD

Remove the skin and bones from the whiting and either pound or rub the flesh through a sieve. Moisten with one or two tablespoonfuls of cream and work in a little lemon juice. Continue working in the remainder of the cream and season well. Place this in the fish and close the dark side over the stuffing so that it does not appear at the cut. A variety of stuffings may be used and one containing shrimps or mushrooms may have a sauce containing the same ingredient served with it.

TROUT WITH BUTTER

INGREDIENTS

3 river trout
2–3 oz. butter
1 tablesp. each of chopped
  capers and chopped
  gherkins

Chopped parsley
Lemon slices or quarters
Sliced gherkins for garnish

METHOD

Clean, wash, and dry the trout, leaving the heads on. Dip in seasoned flour and fry in butter until brown on one side. Turn and brown on the other side. Lift on to a hot serving dish and keep warm. Heat the butter remaining in the pan until it is nut-brown, stir in capers and chopped gherkins to taste, and pour over the fish. Sprinkle with chopped parsley and serve with lemon quarters and slices of gherkin cut several times with scissors to within a quarter-inch of the end to give a fringed effect.

TURBOT

Turbot poached in a little strong fish stock in a moderate oven can be finished with a variety of sauces, each of which imparts a different name to the finished dish. Use one gill of sauce to 1 lb. fish.

TURBOT MORNAY is finished with cheese sauce.

TURBOT BERCY calls for a Bercy sauce which is used chiefly for sole but is also suitable for whiting, brill, halibut, and turbot. It is fairly thin in consistency.

When the turbot is cooked, drain it thoroughly and remove the black skin. Put it on a serving dish and mask with Bercy sauce made as follows:

INGREDIENTS

1 oz. shallot chopped very
  finely
½ oz. butter
⅛ pt white wine
Juice of ¼ lemon

A good ¼ pt fish stock (in
  which the turbot was
  cooked)
Salt and pepper
Herb butter

HERB BUTTER INGREDIENTS

1 teasp. each chopped
  parsley, chervil, tarragon,
  and fennel

¾ oz. butter

METHOD

Cook the shallots in half an ounce of butter until soft but
not brown. Add the wine and fish stock and boil down to
half the volume. Add seasoning and lemon juice and then
work in the herb butter. To make the herb butter, chop all
the herbs finely and wring dry in a clean piece of muslin.
Work the butter with a fork or wooden spoon until creamy
and then beat in the herbs. If fresh herbs are not available
parsley must replace them, but the flavour differs in con-
sequence.

Butter must be used for this sauce. Beginners sometimes
find difficulty in thickening with butter. It is possible to
beat half an ounce of flour with the herb butter and to stir
the whole into the sauce in order to ensure that it thickens.
If this is done, boil the sauce for 1 minute after the butter
mixture has been blended in.

YUGOSLAVIAN BAKED FISH

This is easy to prepare and should be used for fish which
lacks flavour. Fillets of coley or other cheap white fish are
very suitable.

INGREDIENTS

2 lb. filleted fish (free from
   skin)
⅛ pt tomato purée
   (or 1 small tin)
⅛ pt water
6 oz. onions

¼ pt oil
⅛ pt white wine
Pepper and salt
Chopped parsley
Lemon quarters

METHOD

Slice the onions very thinly and cook in oil until tender but
not brown. After a few minutes preliminary cooking the
pan can be covered with a lid so that the onions become
really soft and creamy. Mix the tomato purée, water, and
wine and season with salt and pepper. Pour any surplus fat
off the onions and add the tomato mixture to them. Stir well.
Grease a baking dish and sprinkle with chopped parsley.
Lay the fillets of fish in it and sprinkle generously with
chopped parsley. Pour the tomato mixture over the top,
cover with greased paper, and bake in a moderate oven (375°)
for 30 minutes. Garnish with lemon quarters.

    This dish can be prepared in advance and kept in a cool
place for 3–4 hours before it is baked. For this reason, it is
an excellent choice for a single-handed hostess.

CHAPTER 3

Meat

YOUNG animals give flesh which has less flavour than that from full-grown animals. Veal, for example, has far less flavour than beef. Young carcases consequently need less seasoning, otherwise their delicate flavour may be smothered.

Young meat is also more tender and therefore needs less cooking, but the tenderness depends on the part of the animal.

During its lifetime, an animal uses its muscles, some muscles getting far more exercise than others. Those which are used most give tougher meat than those which are used least. Shin of beef and neck of mutton are tougher than sirloin or loin. The tough cuts require moist cooking (stewing or boiling) for a long time in order to become tender. Alternatively, they may be minced, in which case they will cook more quickly. Really tender cuts can be grilled or fried and are done in a few minutes. In between these two extremes are joints which require a longer cooking time but can be made tender without adding liquid, e.g. shoulder or best end of neck of lamb or round of beef, which are admirable for roasting. There is no reason why such joints should not be boiled if this method of cooking is preferred, e.g. boiled leg of lamb or silverside of beef.

Moderately tough cuts can also be braised. By this means, meat is rendered tender and given a good flavour but it is dry to eat.

*

GRILLED MEAT

If there is doubt about the tenderness of a steak it can be beaten with a rolling pin to break the muscle fibres a little. It is not necessary to do this for a tender piece of meat.

Heat the grill until it is red hot. Grease the bars of the grill pan and brush both surfaces of the meat with melted dripping or oil and season well. Place the meat under the grill and seal on one side until brown. Turn between two palate knives or other blunt utensils (do not perforate the meat) and seal on the other side. Lower the heat and continue to cook until done, turning at two-minute intervals.

Pork and mutton should be well done. Beef can be under-done or rare. Veal is generally well cooked. Ham is cooked until done. The fat round a slice of ham should be slit with scissors at half-inch intervals to prevent a gammon rasher curling up.

Grilled meats are not served with gravy. A piquant sauce or savoury butter usually accompanies them. They are garnished with watercress. Tomatoes and mushrooms are often served with them.

MIXED GRILL

For one person use:

1 loin chop or cutlet of lamb	Seasoning
1 sausage (chipolata for preference)	½ oz. Maître d'hôtel butter (see page 172)
1 sheep's kidney	Potato straws
1 or 2 rashers bacon	Watercress
2 mushrooms	

POTATO STRAWS are cut the size of matchsticks and soaked in cold salted water for 30 minutes. They are then

dried on a cloth and fried in deep fat until very pale. They
are removed from the fat, which is reheated until a faint
haze rises. They are then immersed a second time until
they are golden brown. The single-handed cook can leave
them after the first fry until she is ready to dish up and
then heat the fat and cook them for a second time immediately before use.

THE GRILL

Remove surplus fat and the bone from the chop. Wipe it
with a clean damp cloth and roll it up. Pass a skewer through
it to keep it in shape. Prick the sausage and impale on a
skewer. Wash and dry the kidney, peel off the skin, and slit
almost in two. Remove the core with a knife or scissors.
Place on a skewer. Cut the rind from the bacon and grill
flat or, alternatively, cut the rasher in two and roll up,
putting the bacon rolls on a skewer. Halve the tomatoes. Skin
the mushrooms and remove part of the stalk. Season all these
foods and brush with melted dripping or oil.

Grease the grid of the grill and place the chop and sausage
on it. Cook under a red-hot grill for 3 minutes, turning at
least twice. Add the kidney and grill another 5 minutes. Add
mushrooms, tomatoes, and bacon rolls and continue cooking
until all are tender. Turn the meats frequently.

Arrange on a hot dish with Maître d'hôtel butter sliced
on the meat. Garnish with watercress and small bundles of
potato straws.

FRIED MEAT

Trim off surplus fat and wipe with a clean damp cloth.
Season. Take a heavy frying-pan and heat in it a little
dripping or oil. Pour off the surplus and place the meat in.
Sear over a fast heat on one side for 2 minutes, turn without
perforating the meat and sear the second side for 2 minutes.
Lower the heat and continue to cook gently until done,

turning frequently. Beef may be served underdone, other fried meats are well cooked. Watercress is used to garnish them.

Any juices escaping into the frying-pan are diluted with stock and seasoned with pepper and salt to give a gravy. A little gravy browning is frequently necessary. A teaspoonful of flour to every half-pint of stock is used to thicken the gravy served with mutton and pork. Beefsteak is usually served with fried onions and any juices from the meat are poured over it undiluted.

VEAL CUTLETS FRIED

INGREDIENTS

1 lb. best end of neck of veal	Egg
Butter or oil for frying	Breadcrumbs
1 teasp. chopped parsley	Salt and pepper
Grated zest of ¼ lemon	Watercress
½ teasp. lemon juice	

METHOD

Cut the meat into slices and trim into neat fillets. Cut out the chine bone, at the end where the meat is thickest, and chop off the rib bone so that only about two inches remains. Beat the egg with parsley, lemon juice, lemon zest, and seasoning and dip each cutlet into this mixture and then into breadcrumbs. Fry in hot butter or oil, turning carefully when half cooked. Garnish with watercress.

A brown gravy can be made to serve with this dish or a tomato or brown sauce can be used instead.

Veal fillet in thin slices is cooked in the same way.

WIENER SCHNITZEL

INGREDIENTS

Escalopes of veal (cut from a fillet)

Butter or oil for frying

Egg and breadcrumbs for coating

Egg, anchovy fillets, salt, pepper, and lemon juice

Capers

Lemon slices

METHOD

Have one or two escalopes for each serving, about quarter of an inch thick. Beat them until they are very thin and season both sides with pepper, salt, and lemon juice. Dip in seasoned egg and then in breadcrumbs and fry until golden brown on both sides. Fry one egg per escalope and serve each escalope with an egg on top of it. Lay fillets of anchovy and capers on top of each egg. Garnish with lemon slices. Serve with brown sauce to which some lemon juice has been added.

Escalopes of veal can be grilled and served with equal quantities of butter and cream melted in a double saucepan and seasoned with pepper and salt. They are then called 'à la Normande'. If fried without an egg and breadcrumb coating they can be finished in the same way or sprinkled with grated cheese and breadcrumbs and browned under a hot grill. They are then coated with Madeira sauce and called 'Escalopes Paillard'.

Escalopes may be stuffed and rolled before cooking and are then called Paupiettes, for example, season the meat with pepper, salt, and lemon juice, lay a thin slice of ham on each escalope and then a thick slice of hard-boiled egg. Roll up and tie securely or skewer with a cocktail stick. Cook gently in melted butter until done – about 10 minutes – and then add a little cream. Cover the pan with a lid and then simmer for a few minutes. Correct seasoning and serve with a lemon garnish.

BOILED MEAT

Remove excess fat from the meat, trim it if necessary, remove bone if required, and tie up neatly. When meat is boiled it is plunged into water which is actually at boiling-point and which completely or practically covers the meat. After 5 minutes fast boiling the scum is removed from the top of the liquid, seasoning is added and the heat is reduced so that the water bubbles gently. Skim at intervals.

A bouquet garni and peppercorns may be added to the cooking liquid. Turnips, carrots, and onions are also used to impart flavour to the meat. The cooking liquid has a good flavour and should be used as stock for making soups and gravies. Cooking times vary with the quality and shape of the joint. A more tender cut obviously cooks in a shorter time than a tougher one, though inferior quality meat should be stewed rather than boiled. A boned or thick piece of meat takes longer to cook than one which has a thin layer of meat on the bone, e.g. neck of mutton. A joint under three pounds in weight requires at least an hour. As a very rough guide, any joint over three pounds requires 15 minutes per pound and an extra 15 minutes. Larger joints require a correspondingly shorter cooking time.

If vegetables cooked in the same pot as the meat are to be served with it, they should be put in for the last half-hour of cooking only. If they are there solely to impart flavour, they can be put in with the meat. In this case, they will be overcooked and hence unsuitable to serve.

The meat is drained when done and served on a hot dish with vegetables at either end and parsley as a garnish. Chefs frequently slice the meat before serving it. A sauce accompanies the meat, e.g. boiled mutton – caper sauce (made with cooking liquid or half liquid and half milk):

Boiled beef – a little of its own cooking liquid
Boiled pork – a little of its own cooking liquid
Boiled ham – Madeira sauce

Suet dumplings are served with boiled beef. They should be dropped into the cooking pot half an hour before the meat is served and the water must boil at the moment they are added.

SALT MEAT is placed in cold water and brought to the boil, and this water is thrown away. Boiling water is then poured over the meat and it is cooked as fresh meat. If it has been in pickle for a long time, it is sometimes necessary to soak overnight in cold water to remove some of the salt. Tongue is cooked in the same way. Cooked ham or pork is skinned and dusted with brown breadcrumbs before serving. Tongue is skinned and trimmed.

BOILED FOWL

Clean and truss the bird. Rub the breast with lemon juice and wrap in paper or tie in a greased cloth. Place into boiling water or stock which practically covers the bird, and add a bouquet garni, six peppercorns, one carrot, one turnip, and one onion. Skim well and lower the heat. Cook gently until the bird is done. This is roughly 1 hour for a young boiler and up to 2½ hours for an old one. When it is cooked, remove the trussing string and the skin. Dry with a clean cloth. Serve on a hot dish and coat with parsley or hard-boiled egg sauce made with some of the cooking liquor.

To make the sauce use:

1½ oz. flour
1½ oz. butter
¾ pt stock

1 chopped hard-boiled egg, or
1 dessertsp. chopped
parsley

This sauce must be thick enough to mask the flesh of the bird.

BOILED TURKEY

The breast is usually stuffed with one to two pounds of sausage meat, according to the size of the bird. It is cooked like boiled chicken but for a longer time. It is served with oyster or celery sauce.

CELERY SAUCE: Boil celery in salted water until tender, and chop finely. Stir into a white coating sauce made with milk, or half milk and half turkey stock.

OYSTER SAUCE can be made from tinned oysters. The chopped fish and the liquor from the tin are added to a white sauce made as above. If fresh oysters are used they should be cooked in their own liquor in a covered pan until tender and then chopped. A pint of sauce or more will be required for a large turkey.

Fried forcemeat balls and parsley are used to garnish boiled turkey.

FORCEMEAT

INGREDIENTS

4 tablesps. white breadcrumbs	1 teasp. chopped parsley
2 tablesps. chopped suet, or ¾ oz. melted butter	Grated lemon zest
	Pepper and salt
	1 egg

METHOD

Mix the dry ingredients and add enough egg to bind together. Shape into balls and fry in hot dripping or oil until browned lightly all over. Drain on absorbent paper.

BOILED HAM

Weigh the ham and allow 20 minutes per pound plus an extra 20 minutes for cooking small joints. Hams of twelve pounds or more require 15 minutes per pound and 15 minutes extra.

If you do not like the meat salt, soak in cold water overnight before boiling.

Put the joint into a pan of cold water and gradually bring to the boil; skim frequently. Lower the heat and simmer gently, timing the cooking process from the moment the water boils.

When it is cooked, the rind will peel off easily. Drain for a few moments and then sprinkle with browned breadcrumbs. Serve with parsley or Madeira sauce.

If it is to be served cold, leave the ham in the cooking liquid to cool.

ROAST MEAT

Tough cuts do not roast satisfactorily. Take the joint to be roasted and trim off excess fat. Bone it if desired, roll up, and tie securely. Mutton and pork which have been boned are frequently stuffed before roasting.

STUFFING FOR MUTTON (Boned Shoulder)

½ lb. sausage meat
2 teasps. chopped parsley

1 teasp. finely chopped onion
About 1 tablesp. stock

Mix the ingredients together, pack into the cavity from which the bone was removed and roll up the joint. Tie it securely in a neat shape to facilitate carving.

STUFFING FOR PORK

2 large onions	1 teasp. chopped sage leaves
2 or 2½ oz. breadcrumbs	Pepper and salt
1 oz. melted butter	A little egg to bind

Boil the onions and chop finely, add the remaining ingredients and pack into the meat. Roll up and tie neatly.

STUFFING FOR CHICKEN (Veal Forcemeat)

3 oz. breadcrumbs	¼ teasp. chopped thyme
1 oz. chopped suet, or	and marjoram
melted butter	Egg and milk to bind
2 teasps. chopped parsley	

METHOD

Mix all the ingredients together. Do not make the forcemeat too wet. Pack into the breast of the bird and secure the neck flap over the stuffing with a small skewer.

Extra stuffing may be put in the body cavity if desired. A little grated lemon zest can be added to this stuffing.

STUFFING FOR TURKEY

½ pt chestnuts	½ teasp. chopped mixed
2 oz. melted butter	herbs, or a pinch of dried
¼ lb. sausage meat	herbs
2 oz. breadcrumbs	Pepper and salt

METHOD

Slit the skins of the chestnuts and put them in a tin in the oven until the skins are brittle. Remove the skins. Either sieve or mince the chestnuts and add to them the remaining ingredients.

Sausage meat can be omitted from this recipe and in this case one to two pounds of sausage meat is used to stuff the breast of the bird and the chestnut stuffing is put in the body cavity. Alternatively, veal forcemeat can be put into the body, up to one and a half pounds of crumbs being required according to the size of the bird.

When meat is ready to roast it should be wiped with a damp cloth and weighed so that cooking time can be estimated. A joint weighing up to three pounds requires at least an hour. Over this weight an approximation of the cooking time is given as follows:

Mutton – 15–20 minutes per pound and 20 minutes extra.

Veal and Pork – 25 minutes per pound and 25 minutes extra.

Beef – 15 minutes per pound and 15 minutes extra.

Chicken – 40 minutes upwards according to size.

Turkey – generally cooked gently for 25 minutes per pound and 25 minutes extra.

Boned meat requires 5 minutes per pound more than the same joint unboned.

These times are only approximate, because the shape and size of the joint, the amount of bone, the temperature of the oven, and the tenderness of the meat all influence the speed with which it cooks. For example, large joints require less time for each pound than small ones.

Heat some dripping in an oven at 425° and place the meat in it. Baste well. Allow to sear at this temperature for 15 minutes. Baste again and turn if you wish. Lower the heat to 375° or 350° for the remainder of the cooking time. When done, serve on a hot dish and garnish with watercress. Pour off the fat from the roasting tin, retaining any juices from the meat. Dilute with half a pint of good stock for every three pounds of meat and stir until boiling. Season well and add a little gravy browning if necessary. Remove any grease from the top and serve in a gravy-boat.

For mutton, lamb, pork, chicken, and turkey thicken the gravy with one heaped teaspoonful flour to half a pint of stock. Stir the flour into the roasting tin and brown slightly, and then add the stock gradually, stirring all the time.

There is a growing tendency to roast meat in an oven at 325° throughout the cooking period. The surface does not get so brown and crisp and cooking times are considerably longer.

It is possible to pot-roast small joints. A heavy pan with a thick machined base and a well-fitting lid is needed. The dripping is heated in this pan and the joint placed in. It is browned all over and the lid is put on the pan and the heat reduced. Cooking is completed without raising the heat. Potatoes will roast round the meat as they will in an oven.

Roast chicken is cooked with slices of fat bacon on the breast to prevent it drying out. The bacon can be removed about 20 minutes before the bird is done. Game birds and turkey are usually treated in the same way.

BAKED HAM

Ham is often baked in an oven wrapped in a pastry crust or in a sheet of aluminium foil. Work and ingredients are saved if foil is used instead of pastry. The joint should be wrapped completely in foil with the dull side outwards and cooked in a tin. Cook in a moderately hot oven till tender. It is usual to allow 20 minutes per pound plus 20 minutes extra for small hams, and 15 minutes per pound plus 15 minutes extra for hams over twelve pounds. It must be remembered that metal foil reflects heat and slows up the cooking process so that additional cooking time must be allowed to compensate for this.

FINISHING BAKED HAM

When cooked, remove the rind and dust the surface with brown breadcrumbs or brush with glaze. In America, it is customary to score the fat into squares or diamonds and to press a clove into the centre of each. Brown sugar is then sprinkled liberally over the surface and the ham is returned to the oven for 15 minutes, so that the surface gets brown. More flavour is given if grated orange zest is mixed with the sugar. Yet another alternative is to mix the brown sugar with a little dry mustard, ground cloves and ground cinnamon before rubbing it over the surface of the ham. Thick slices of pineapple heated round the ham in the sugary liquid which runs from it can be served on the same dish. Put a cherry in the centre of each pineapple slice.

Many recipes suggest cooking ham for half the required time in boiling water and then putting it in the oven. This is done to reduce the saltiness and the flavour, both of which are preserved by baking.

BRAISING MEAT

Braising is a method of cookery which imparts a good flavour to food and renders it very tender but dry. It can be used for joints or for liver or ham. Tough meats are not suitable for braising. A heavy pan can be used to braise foods on top of the stove or a casserole to braise them in the oven. In either case a well-fitting lid is necessary, and it is advisable to put a sheet of greased paper between the pan and the lid to keep in steam.

A mirepoix is first prepared. This consists of coarsely diced onions, shallots, carrots and turnips, bacon rinds or lean bacon, and a little celery. All of these are fried in dripping until browned all over, and then they are laid on the bed of the braising pot. The meat is browned in the same dripping and lifted out and put on top of the vegetables. A bouquet garni is added to the vegetables, and sufficient brown stock to come nearly, but not quite, to the top of the vegetables. Some fresh tomato can be put in the pan. Paper and a lid are put on and the pan is placed in a slow oven, 325°, or on a low flame. The meat cooks in steam, and the veget ables impart some flavour to the meat and a great deal to the gravy. Basting should take place at frequent intervals. When the meat is done, it is lifted on to a hot serving dish and the gravy is strained. A little arrowroot or cornflour is used to thicken it only very slightly, and gravy browning may be added. It is then stirred until boiling and poured over the meat. Watercress is used for the garnish.

There are several variations and modifications in the basic recipe. If a large piece of meat is being braised, a calf's foot should sit among the mirepoix. This thickens the gravy and means that arrowroot is unnecessary. Since a clear glossy sauce is required, calf's foot is ideal. The meat from the calf's foot is diced and replaced in the sauce before serving.

Topside, flank of beef, chuck rib, or shoulder beef are often braised, as are pieces of veal and other cuts lacking fat. These need larding before cooking. Strips of fat bacon are threaded through them with a larding needle at intervals of one and a half to two inches.

Ideally, meat is marinaded before braising. It is put in a shallow container and surrounded with red wine in which raw carrot and turnip have been sliced; peppercorns, a bay leaf, thyme, and parsley are also added. The meat is left in this marinade for 24 hours and turned every 6 hours. If salt is added the wine will be spoiled.

Salt-beef can be braised after soaking in water overnight to remove some of the salt.

A whole shoulder or leg of mutton, or a loin of lamb, can be braised. Larding is not necessary here as the joint is not lacking in fat. Stock is not added to the mirepoix since enough juice escapes from the meat to provide liquid for basting. Joints can be left on the bone, or boned and stuffed.

Small pieces of topside, buttock steak, or liver are often cooked this way and so are fish and some vegetables, e.g. celery and lettuce. Birds too may be braised.

The average cooking time is 20–25 minutes for each pound, and 20 minutes extra for large joints. A slice of topside weighing one to one and a half pounds requires one and a half hours to become tender, and liver cut in a thick slice takes as long.

STEWING

Stewing is generally used to render tough cuts tender. The meat is trimmed and excess fat is removed. It is then cut into cubes of about a two-inch size. If it is cut very finely it will be dry and flavourless when tender. The meat is fried in dripping to brown all its surfaces and then is put into boiling stock to which vegetables, a bouquet garni, and seasoning have been added. It is skimmed and then the heat is lowered and the stew simmers gently until cooked. Thickening may be added at the end of the cooking period or the correct amount of flour to thicken the stock used for a stew may be sprinkled into the pan when frying is completed and before the stock has been added.

Stews may be white (blanquette), golden (fricassee), or brown. Chicken and white meats are often made into white stews. Lamb is steeped in water to remove the blood. All these meats may be blanched before being used for a blanquette. In order to keep the stew white, preliminary frying is generally omitted, and only white vegetables are used, e.g. onions and button mushrooms. White stock is used and sometimes milk is added. When the sauce is thickened at the end of the cooking time, it is usual for eggs and cream to be incorporated, with or without flour as well.

Fricassees are made with chicken, rabbit, veal, or lamb. In this case the meat is fried until golden. In addition, onions and mushrooms may also be fried until golden and flour may then be sprinkled into the pan and also fried until golden. The final colour of the thickened sauce is a pale beige. Eggs and cream are often stirred in after cooking is completed and the pan has been removed from the heat. They serve to thicken the sauce and to give it a superior flavour and texture. In economical cookery they are omitted and extra flour is used.

In blanquettes and fricassees, there should be no dark or coloured vegetables. For this reason carrots are not added. Button mushrooms should be used, but if large or field mushrooms must be used the dark gills are first shaved off. These can be kept to flavour stocks and soups.

Brown stews take their colour from the preliminary frying given to the meat and vegetables, both of which are well browned in fat. Flour is frequently browned in the fat. The brown stock used for cooking as well as gravy browning added before serving also give colour. Beef and mutton are both used for brown stews and there are recipes for chicken, veal, rabbit, hare, and game birds.

Some stews have special ingredients and take their name according to these additions: e.g. Hungarian goulash has paprika and aniseed in it. Carbonade of beef has beer in (originally this term meant grill, but time has altered the meaning, to the horror of the purists).

Stews can usually be cooked in a casserole in the oven or in a stewpan or casserole on top of the stove.

Very thin small strips of topside, flank, or even rump steak are often spread with veal forcemeat, rolled up, and tied into shape and then stewed. This dish is called Beef Olives.

BEEF OLIVES

INGREDIENTS

1 lb. rump steak or good
   quality stewing steak
A little carrot, turnip, and
   onion
¾ pt brown stock

Bouquet garni
1 oz. flour
¾ oz. dripping
Gravy browning

FORCEMEAT INGREDIENTS

2 oz. breadcrumbs   1/2 oz. melted butter
1 teasp. chopped parsley   Pepper and salt
Pinch of mixed herbs   Egg to bind

METHOD

Wipe the meat and cut into very thin slices. Cut the slices
into strips about two inches by three inches. Spread each
one with forcemeat and roll it up. Tie securely with thin
string. Heat the dripping in a stewpan and fry the beef
olives and vegetables until brown. Pour off any surplus fat.
Add the stock, bouquet garni, and seasoning and bring
quickly to the boil. Skim and then lower the heat and simmer
until the meat is tender. The time will depend on the quality
of the meat used, from 40 minutes to 2 hours. Remove the
string and dish the meat. Blend the flour with a little cold
stock and stir this into the pan. Stir until boiling. Correct
the seasoning, add gravy browning if necessary, and strain
over the meat. Garnish with chopped parsley and freshly
cooked diced carrots and turnips.

METHOD FOR FORCEMEAT

Mix all the ingredients using only enough egg to moisten
slightly.

BLANQUETTE OF VEAL

INGREDIENTS

1 lb. fillet veal (pie meat will   A bouquet garni
   make a cheaper stew)   1 egg yolk
3 oz. button mushrooms (or   3/4 pt white stock
   the white caps of large   1/4 pt milk
   ones)   1 teasp. lemon juice
3 oz. button onions   3 tablesps. cream

2 oz. butter   Bacon rolls
1 oz. flour   Chopped parsley
4 tablesps. dry white wine   Pepper and salt

METHOD

Wipe the meat and cut into neat pieces. Slice the mushrooms.

Put the stock, wine, veal, mushrooms, onions, and bouquet garni into a stewpan and bring quickly to the boil. Skim, reduce the heat, and simmer gently until done (up to 1½ hours according to the meat used). Melt the butter in a pan and add the flour. Fry until sandy in texture but not coloured at all. Gradually stir in the milk and half a pint of the stock in which the veal was cooked and stir until boiling. The remaining stock can be added if the consistency is too thick. Add the cooked veal, mushrooms, and onions. Correct the seasoning and stir in lemon juice. Remove from the heat and cool a little. Mix the egg yolk and cream, and stir them into the cool sauce. Reheat gently but do not boil. Serve on a hot dish with bacon rolls and chopped parsley to garnish.

This recipe can be adapted to give an economical meal if only two or three mushrooms are used, and if the egg yolk and cream are omitted. In this case more flour will be needed – probably another ounce. Wine can also be omitted, but it gives a subtle taste which should not be foregone if possible. Chicken or other white meat can be used in place of veal.

Fricassee of veal can be made with the same ingredients but by a different method. The butter is put into the stewpan and heated. The meat and vegetables are then fried in it until golden brown. The flour is sprinkled into the pan and also cooked until golden brown. Then the stock and bouquet garni are added and the whole is stirred until boiling and then simmered until tender. Finish off with lemon juice, eggs, and cream. Remove the bouquet garni before serving.

BRAISED LAMB À LA BOUQUETIÈRE
(A DRY BRAISE)

INGREDIENTS

Loin or any other joint of
    lamb
12 oz. carrots
12 oz. turnips
8 oz. onions
Bouquet garni
2 oz. dripping

Stock
Gravy browning
Arrowroot
Pepper and salt
Bacon rinds
Chopped parsley

GARNISH INGREDIENTS

Green peas
French beans
Cauliflower sprigs coated
    with cheese sauce and
    grilled
Tomatoes stuffed with
    cooked onion and
    mushroom

Slices of turnip with spinach
    purée on top
Piped potato whirls
Carrots and turnips diced
    and boiled and tossed in
    butter, or any other
    vegetable previously
    cooked and in small pieces

METHOD

Bone and stuff the joint of meat, or leave it on the bone.
Melt the dripping in a roasting tin or casserole and fry in
it the bacon rinds, carrots, turnips, and onions all cut into
large dice. For a large joint of meat it may be necessary to
use a greater quantity of mirepoix.

When the vegetables are brown, pour off most of the
remaining fat, add the bouquet garni, and put the meat on
top of the vegetables. Season the meat and vegetables and
then cover the roasting tin with a closely fitting lid. Do
not add any liquid. Place into an oven at 375°. Baste the
meat and turn it over at frequent intervals. Allow 25 minutes

for each pound and 25 minutes extra for an unboned joint, and 30 minutes for each pound and 30 minutes for a boned one.

When the meat is quite done, put it on a hot dish and keep in a warm place for 5 minutes. Then untie the string round a boned joint and cut it into slices. If it is not left to rest for 5 minutes, it will uncurl when it is carved. Lay the slices down the centre of a very large dish, overlapping each other.

While the meat rests make the gravy. Pour off any fat from the tin and discard the vegetables. Add about half a pint of stock blended with two teaspoonfuls of arrowroot to the meat juice in the tin and stir until boiling. Add gravy browning and seasoning. Pour this over the meat – it should not be a thick sauce. Put the separately prepared 'bouquets' of garnish vegetables at intervals all round the edges of the dish, and garnish with chopped parsley.

This dish looks delightful but the time and work involved are considerable. For family catering it may be better to serve the braised meat without this garnish.

If a calf's foot can be procured to be cooked in the bed of the roasting tin, arrowroot is not necessary.

BRAISED PIGEON

INGREDIENTS

2 pigeons	Bacon rinds and larding bacon
2 carrots	½ pt stock
2 onions	2 tablesps. sherry or Marsala
1 turnip	Gravy browning
Dripping	1 slice fried bread with the crusts removed
Lemon juice	
4 peppercorns	Garnish of watercress, and cooked peas and carrots
Bouquet garni	

METHOD

Pigeons can be cooked empty or they can be stuffed with a forcemeat of breadcrumbs, minced chicken livers, and mushrooms bound together with equal quantities of egg and stock.

Clean and truss the pigeons and lard the breast. Stuff if they are to be cooked with stuffing in. Slice the carrot, turnip, and onion and put into an earthenware dish. Add the bouquet garni, lemon juice, and red wine, and lay the pigeons in this mixture. Turn every 6 hours for 24 hours. Complete this dish as follows:

Brown the birds in hot fat, drain the vegetables well, and lay them in a casserole or heavy pan. Add the bouquet garni, bacon rinds, and enough stock barely to cover the vegetables. Place the pigeons on top. If the breast meat has not been larded, lay strips of fat bacon over the breast. Cover the whole with greased paper and then with a lid. Cook gently in a slow oven (325°) or in a pan on top of the stove, for 40–60 minutes, until the birds are tender. Baste at intervals while cooking.

Fry a slice of bread and place on the serving dish. Remove the trussing string from the pigeons and put them on the fried bread. Strain the liquor from the braise and cook quickly to reduce its volume by a third or a half. If it is not thick enough, add a teaspoonful of blended arrowroot and stir until boiling. Add gravy browning if necessary and correct the seasoning. Remove any grease and pour the gravy round the birds. Garnish with watercress and a few freshly boiled peas and diced carrots at each end of the dish.

BRAISED LIVER

INGREDIENTS

1¼ lb. liver in one thick piece	1 oz. dripping
	Bouquet garni

2 carrots	½–¾ pt stock
2 onions	Arrowroot
1 turnip	Gravy browning
1 stick celery	Pepper, salt, and parsley
Bacon rinds or ham rinds	

METHOD

Cut the vegetables into rather large pieces. Heat the dripping in a heavy pan or a casserole, and fry the vegetables and bacon rinds until browned. Remove them and keep them hot. Wash, skin, and dry the liver. Fry lightly and drain off the surplus fat. Replace the vegetables and put the liver on top of them, add the bouquet garni and enough stock barely to cover the vegetables. Season, cover with greased paper and then a lid, and cook in a slow oven (325°), until tender, or on top of the stove (approximately 1 hour). Baste at intervals.

Finish the gravy as for braised pigeons. Serve the liver on a dish with the gravy strained over it and garnish with parsley.

The liver can be stuffed. A forcemeat is made with:

1 oz. breadcrumbs	1 teasp. chopped parsley
1 oz. chopped ham	Seasoning
1 teasp. very finely chopped onion	A little stock to moisten

A slit is made in the liver, the forcemeat is packed in and the edges of the slit sewn together.

This recipe is suitable for small pieces of beef, or for heart. It can also be used for other foods such as celery or cabbage stuffed with sausage meat. The cooking time will vary with the different foods.

BRAINS

Calf's, sheep's, or pig's brains can be used. Remove the skin and wash in clean water and then wash several times in salted water. After this treatment, they can be cooked and served in several ways.

SCRAMBLED BRAINS

Parboil the brains in salted water containing the juice of half a lemon, a slice of onion, a bay leaf, and six peppercorns. Drain them and chop into small pieces. Beat up four eggs, add a quarter teaspoonful of chilli vinegar, pepper and salt, and an ounce of melted butter. Stir in the chopped brains and heat this mixture over a slow flame, stirring all the time, until the egg is scrambled.

FRIED BRAINS

Marinade the brains for 1 hour in one dessertspoonful of oil, one-eighth of a pint of white wine, four tablespoonfuls of vinegar, two slices of onion, and a bouquet garni. Season the mixture well and turn the brains in it several times during the hour. Dry them and then dip in seasoned flour. Fry in hot dripping or oil until brown. If it is felt that the flavour is insipid, a clove of garlic can be added to the marinade. Alternatively, a little onion can be fried in dripping, and removed before the brains are fried.

BRAWN

INGREDIENTS

½ *pig's head* (approximately 6 lb.)	1 *pig's trotter*
	A few leaves of sage
1 *lb. steak*	*Pepper*

METHOD

Wash the head and the trotter very well in several salted waters. Cut up the steak. Place all the meat in a pan and add water to come half-way up. Add sage and seasoning and then bring quickly to the boil. Skim well, lower the heat, cover with a lid, and simmer gently until tender (about 4 hours). Take out the sage. Remove the meat from the bones and chop it up and cut the steak into small pieces. Return the cut meat to the stock and boil rapidly for a few minutes. Correct the seasoning. Put the meat into a mould and cover with stock. Allow to get cold. Turn out and serve with salad.

It is wise to add very little salt at the beginning because there is a good deal of evaporation in 4 hours and the brawn may get too salty. Taste the stock before pouring it into the mould.

BROWN STEW

INGREDIENTS

1 lb. beef (chuck, shin, or buttock), or mutton (neck or shoulder), or rabbit (cut into joints)	1 turnip
	1 oz. dripping
	¾ pt stock
	Bouquet garni
2 carrots	¾ oz. flour
1 onion, or	Seasoning
6 shallots	Gravy browning

METHOD

Wipe the meat and remove any fat. Cut in two-inch cubes or into joints if rabbit is used. Cut the vegetables into one-inch cubes. Melt the dripping in the stewpan and fry the vegetables until brown, turning with a spoon all the time. Remove the meat and vegetables and keep them hot. Add the flour to the pan and fry with incessant stirring until the flour is the colour of milk chocolate. Add the stock at once or the flour will over cook and taste bitter. Bring to the boil and add the bouquet garni and seasoning. Replace the meat and vegetables, cover with a lid and simmer gently until done (1½–2½ hours according to the meat used). Correct seasoning, consistency, and colour. Put the meat on a serving dish and strain the gravy over it. Garnish with parsley. The vegetables in this stew are used only to impart flavour, and they are not served.

A more economical and homely stew is prepared by adding the carrot and turnip 45 minutes before the stew is served, and then pouring the whole contents of the pan (except the bouquet garni) on to the serving dish. For this stew, the vegetables should be cut into regular, neat pieces.

CHICKEN CHAUDFROID

(See mayonnaise of fish for details of preparation.)

INGREDIENTS

1 cooked chicken	3 gills of white chaudfroid sauce

DECORATION: *Truffle, red pepper, chervil, cucumber skins.*

GARNISH: *Salad and chopped aspic jelly.*

METHOD

Cut the chicken into joints, remove the skin, and chop off the ends of the bones. Lay on a rack and dry with a clean cloth. Chill in a refrigerator. Coat with chaudfroid sauce and leave to set. Coat again if necessary. Dip the decorations into liquid aspic and place on the joints with the point of a needle. Chill until set. Glaze with cold aspic jelly and chill. Lay chicken joints in the centre of a dish and put small pieces of salad vegetable and cut aspic round the edges of the dish.

CHAUDFROID SAUCE

½ pt Béchamel sauce	1 tablesp. cream
1 gill aspic (made double strength)	Seasoning

Cool the sauce and aspic jelly and mix together while still liquid. Season well and pass through a fine sieve. Stir in the cream. Allow to get cold and use when beginning to thicken.

The aspic jelly used for this sauce should be made up double the normal strength, but the aspic used for the glaze should be normal strength.

GRILLED CHICKEN

Use a small spring chicken about two pounds in weight. Raise the skin at the neck end, and scrape the meat from the wishbone. Put the point of the knife underneath this bone and lift it right out. Cut the leg one inch below the knee joints to sever the sinews. Make a slit in the flesh at the side of the bird and bend the knee so that the leg can be tucked right into this hole with the end of the bone sticking out. Cut between the breast and the backbone and sever the skin between the legs. The whole breast can then be pulled away from the carcass to remain attached only at the tail end of the bird. Turn the bird over and beat with a rolling-pin to break the bones and flatten it (if this is not done the bird will curl up when it is heated under the grill). Brush with oil and season well. Cook under a red-hot grill until seared and then lower the heat to complete cooking, or else put into a moderate oven (350°). The chicken resembles a frog when prepared like this; a slice of hard-boiled egg surmounted by a small piece of truffle or pickled walnut can be used to make 'eyes'.

Serve with watercress and a savoury butter.

CHICKEN MARYLAND

Use a tender chicken about two to two and a half pounds in weight. Cut into joints and remove the skin. Season with salt and pepper, dip into beaten egg and then into breadcrumbs.

Grease a roasting tin very well with butter or dripping and put the joints in. Bake in a hot oven (420°) for 30 minutes. After the first 5 minutes baste with two ounces of melted butter. Instead of cooking in an oven, chicken Maryland can be fried. Have enough butter in a frying-pan to come half-way up the chicken and fry for 30–40 minutes turning it once. Cover for half the cooking time. If required crisp, remove the cover for the last half. If not to be crisp, cover for the last half of the cooking time.

ROAST CHICKEN

A young chicken is usually cooked without stuffing. Season inside and out and put a knob of butter inside the bird. Strips of fat bacon are laid on the breast and greased paper placed over the bacon. The bird is put into hot dripping or butter in a roasting tin and cooked about 40 minutes to 1 hour (see roast meat). It can be basted at intervals and a few minutes before it is done, the bacon and paper are removed to allow the breast to brown. If bacon is not used, commence cooking with the bird on its side in the hot fat for 15 minutes and then turn to the other side for 15 minutes and finally place breast upwards until done. This browns the whole of the surface evenly.

Serve it on a hot dish with a watercress garnish. Make gravy with stock from the giblets.

A larger bird is often stuffed with forcemeat (see roast meat) and cooked in the same way for up to 2 hours, according to the size. Chipolata sausage and bacon rolls are placed at either end of the serving dish.

PHEASANT is roasted in the same way as chicken and requires from 40 minutes to 1 hour. It is served on a bread croûte. The feet are left on, only the toes being removed. The ends of the tail feathers can be wrapped in foil and replaced to garnish the pheasant. *Partridge and grouse* require 20–25 minutes roasting time and are also served on a bread croûte.

PIGEONS are roasted similarly and take 40–50 minutes. Many of the pigeons sold today are not tender enough for roasting and should be casseroled.

DUCK must be basted and preferably turned very frequently whilst cooking, so as to get a crisp brown surface. It should be served well done and a three and a half pound duckling usually requires 1½ hours. Ducks may be stuffed with sage and onion stuffing. Apple sauce accompanies stuffed or unstuffed duck; orange salad or bigarade sauce are excellent with unstuffed duck.

WILD DUCK and WIDGEON are apt to taste fishy and it is sometimes recommended that a quarter-inch of boiling water is put in the roasting tin. An onion can be placed inside the body cavity. The birds are cooked in water for 10 minutes with frequent basting. This reduces the fishy taste. The water is then drained off and hot dripping used to complete the cooking in the normal way. Wild duck should be underdone or the flavour is lost. Twenty minutes is considered sufficient time to make them edible, but 35 minutes is not excessive for many tastes.

Watercress is used as a garnish and bigarade or orange sauce as an accompaniment. A good brown gravy can be used in place of orange sauce, in which case orange salad or cranberry jelly is also served.

CURRIED MEAT

The purist scorns curry powder and mixes his own from the many spices which may be blended together to form curry.

The average domestic kitchen, however, is generally equipped with curry powder and with curry paste. The latter improves the flavour and colour of a curry. Curry sauce for meat can be prepared from:

¾ pt well-flavoured stock
2 oz. butter, margarine, or
    dripping
1 tablesp. curry powder
1 teasp. curry paste
4 oz. onion
2–3 oz. sour apple
1 oz. flour

1 tablesp. desiccated or
    freshly grated coconut
1 dessertsp. black treacle
1 oz. sultanas or raisins
1 tomato or a tablesp. tomato
    purée
2 teasps. lemon juice
Salt and pepper

GARNISH: *Parsley and paprika pepper.*

This amount of sauce can be used with one or one and a half pounds of meat, trimmed and free from excess fat, and cut into two-inch cubes.

METHOD

Chop the apple and onion nearly as finely as powder. Melt the fat in a thick pan, and fry the apple and onion until coloured. Stir in curry powder, paste, and flour. Continue to fry, with constant stirring, until the flour is a golden colour. Gradually add stock, seasoning, lemon juice, coconut, and treacle. Bring to the boil, stirring constantly; lower the heat and put on a lid. Simmer for 40 minutes. Skin the tomato, remove the seeds, and chop the flesh into very small pieces. Add this and the washed sultanas after 30 minutes. Correct the seasoning and consistency before serving. This is a basic curry sauce.

If raw meat is to be curried it should be fried in the melted fat before the curry sauce is started. Remove the meat and keep it hot while the sauce is made and then return it to cook in the sauce until it is tender.

Cold meat can be curried. To do this, make the curry sauce and cook it for 40 minutes, then add the cubes of cooked meat and continue to simmer gently until the meat is hot but not overcooked.

Curry is served inside a border of plain boiled rice, or else rice is passed separately. Paprika and parsley are used to garnish the rice.

A sweet chutney, frequently mango chutney, is served with curry.

CURRY OF BEEF (DRY)

Dry curries come from India. For this recipe, tender juicy beef is required. For a normal curry, a less tender cut is satisfactory.

INGREDIENTS

1 lb. tender beef	1 teasp. curry paste
1 oz. butter, margarine, or dripping	1 teasp. sieved chutney
	2 gherkins
2 shallots	2 teasps. lemon juice
1 tablesp. curry powder	Salt

METHOD

Cut the meat into cubes and fry it in the hot fat in a thick pan. Remove and keep hot. Chop the shallots, apple, and gherkins very finely and fry these in the hot fat, but do not allow to get brown. Add the meat, curry powder, paste, chutney, and the lemon juice, and stir over a slow heat until some juice from the meat escapes and forms a gravy. Season and cover with a lid. Simmer very gently until the meat is tender (45 minutes to 1 hour) and then serve. A tablespoon of cream can be stirred in just before serving. Garnish with parsley and red pepper.

COQ AU VIN

Although this recipe calls for a roasting chicken it *can* be made (less satisfactorily) with a young boiler, provided that cooking time is extended to make the flesh really tender.

INGREDIENTS

1 roasting chicken about
   3 lb.
4 oz. green bacon or salt
   pork
20 button onions
1–2 cloves garlic according
   to taste
1½ oz. butter
2 tablesps. olive oil

½–¾ oz. flour
Bouquet garni plus a very
   tiny piece of blade mace
Salt and pepper
3 oz. button mushrooms
½ bottle of good red wine
2 tablesps. brandy
Parsley

(*The equivalent weight of dried mushrooms can replace the button mushrooms. Soak them in water for at least 20 minutes before using.*)

METHOD

Dice the bacon and cut the chicken into portions of suitable size for serving. Put one ounce of butter, the oil, and the diced bacon into a heavy pan and fry until the bacon becomes golden brown. Add the mushrooms and onions, and continue to cook until the onions begin to look transparent. Lift from the pan and keep hot in a casserole. Season the flour and roll the pieces of chicken in it. Brown on both sides in the hot fat and then put into the casserole with any juice which has escaped during frying. Keep the rest of the flour and work into the remaining half ounce of butter. Put all the remaining ingredients except the brandy into the casserole and add seasoning. Cover with a lid and cook in a moderate oven (350°) until the chicken is nearly tender. Remove the chicken, bacon, and vegetables and keep warm while the casserole is put over a high flame to reduce the volume of liquid in it by half. Put in the blended flour and butter and stir until the sauce thickens. Correct the seasoning. Ignite the brandy in a spoon and pour it into the casserole. After it has flamed for a minute stir the pan to extinguish the flame.

Put the chicken, bacon, and vegetables back in the casserole and replace the lid. Put the casserole in the oven to simmer gently (325°) for 45 minutes. When it is ready for serving remove the bouquet garni and put a spray of parsley on top.

DUCK WITH ORANGE

This recipe, like the preceding one, is useful for a dinner party, since all preparation can be completed about an hour before it has to be dished. When it is required, all that is necessary is to lift it from the oven on to a serving dish.

INGREDIENTS

1 duck weighing about 4 lb.	⅛ pt red wine
2 tablesps. brandy	1 tablesp. redcurrant jelly
1 oz. mushrooms	1 dessertsp. tomato purée
3 oranges	Salt and pepper
2 oz. oil	Bouquet garni
½ oz. flour	Chopped parsley
½ pt good brown stock	

METHOD

Cut the duck into portions for serving. Heat the oil in a thick pan and brown the duck on all sides. Pour off surplus oil and stir in the brandy. Remove the duck and put it into a casserole. Slice the mushrooms and put them into the pan. Cook gently for 2–3 minutes. Grate the zest from one orange and add this to the pan. Gently work in the flour and then the tomato purée. Gradually work the stock into this mixture and stir until it boils. Correct the seasoning, add the juice of two oranges and a tablespoonful of redcurrant jelly. Continue stirring until the jelly has melted. Pour this sauce over the duck, add a bouquet garni, and put a lid on the casserole.

Simmer in a slow oven (325°) until the duck is tender. A very young bird should be cooked in an hour – an older one may take nearly 2 hours. Lift the joints on to a serving dish, remove the bouquet garni, and pour the sauce over them. Peel the third orange and cut into wafer-thin slices. Arrange these round the dish and put a thin line of chopped parsley neatly across the centre of each slice, using the blade of a knife to pick up and to place it.

GALANTINE OF BEEF

INGREDIENTS

¾ lb. best quality stewing steak or buttock steak
¼ lb. lean ham
Pepper and salt
1½ oz. breadcrumbs
1 dessertsp. chopped parsley
1 teasp. chopped fresh herbs (tarragon, chervil, and basil), or
A pinch of dried mixed herbs
1 egg mixed with a little stock

METHOD

Wipe the meat and ham, removing all fat and gristle, and then mince them. Add all the other ingredients, using only enough egg and stock to bind together. Place into a greased stone jam-jar or a prepared pudding cloth. Steam for 2–2½ hours.

Serve hot or cold. Hot galantine should be removed from the jar or pudding cloth and rolled in browned crumbs. A good brown sauce should accompany it.

Cold galantine should be allowed to cool and then be brushed with glaze and served with salad.

It is usual to press the galantine to a good shape if it is to be served cold. This is done in the following way:

If a pudding cloth is used, unwrap the galantine while hot and rewrap carefully in a clean cloth so that there are no pleats in the cloth. Press the galantine between two dishes with weights on top. When quite cold unwrap it and wipe any grease from the surface with a cloth wrung out in boiling water and brush with meat glaze or pour on cold aspic jelly.

If a jam-jar is used, slide the galantine out while it is still warm and it will not stick to the jar. It can then be allowed to cool in its cylindrical shape or can be wrapped in a cloth and pressed. Wipe any grease from the surface and glaze it before serving.

GOULASH

This is made with half-inch cubes of raw beef, veal, or chicken. A good quality stewing beef or pie veal will do or prime quality meat can be used.

INGREDIENTS

1 lb. beef	1 clove garlic
6 oz. onion	Bouquet garni
½ oz. paprika pepper (less if a mild flavour is required)	Coffeespoonful crushed aniseed
	Stock
2 oz. fat bacon	Pepper and salt
1 oz. flour	

METHOD

Chop the bacon into small pieces and chop the onion coarsely. Fry them gently to a golden brown colour with the clove of garlic present. Add meat and fry quickly until golden brown. Sprinkle the flour and paprika over the meat, mix well, and fry for a few moments. Add stock barely to cover the meat and bring to the boil. Add seasoning, a bouquet garni, and the aniseed. Simmer with the lid on until the meat is tender (45 minutes to 1½ hours). Remove the garlic and bouquet garni, correct the seasoning, and serve.

A little tomato purée can be added to the goulash. The dish can be cooked in a casserole and served in it.

HOTPOT OF BACON

INGREDIENTS

1 lb. cooking apples	8 rashers bacon
½ lb. onions	8 oz. tomatoes
1 green pepper	¼ pt stock
(seeds removed)	Pepper and salt
8 oz. liver	

Peel and chop the pepper, apple, and onion. Skin and dice the liver. Put the pepper, apple, and onion on the bottom of the casserole and cover with liver. Skin and slice the tomatoes and lay these on top. Season each layer as it is put in the casserole. Remove the bacon rind and lay the rashers on top of the tomatoes. Pour the stock into the dish, until the level is just below the bacon, cover with greased paper and a lid, and place into an oven at 350° for about 1½ hours. Just before serving, the lid can be removed and the bacon crisped under a grill. Garnish with parsley.

HOTPOT OF MUTTON

The traditional hotpot has sliced potato in layers between the meat. Potato may be replaced by carrot or other root vegetables.

INGREDIENTS

1 lb. sliced shoulder of mutton	¼ lb. onion
	Pepper and salt
1 lb. carrots or other root vegetables	Stock or water

This dish can be made with neck of mutton but is then apt to be very greasy and rather full of bone. If neck is used trim off all excess fat.

METHOD

Wipe the meat and cut into neat pieces. Peel and slice the carrots. Chop the onions. Place a layer of meat in a casserole and sprinkle with onion, cover with a layer of carrots and continue until the dish is full, having carrots on top. Add stock barely to cover and season well. Cover with greased paper and put on the lid. Bring to the boil in a moderately hot oven (375°) and then lower the heat and simmer gently for 2–2½ hours at 325°. Remove the paper and lid, wipe the sides of the dish clean, and lay a parsley garnish on the carrot.

The dish is improved by slicing a peeled potato on top of the casserole and putting scraps of mutton fat on the potato. If the potato does not brown in the oven it can be browned under a hot grill just before serving.

KEBABS

Kebabs hail from the Middle East and have long been used in Egypt, Turkey and in Oriental countries. They have now become popular here, and are served in the dining-room and also at outdoor barbecues. Lamb is the meat traditionally used, but poetic licence now seems to permit an individual choice of foods to be put on a skewer and be cooked by grilling. Long skewers of stainless steel are required.

Small pieces of tender lamb cut into cubes or strips about one and a half inches long and one inch wide are threaded on a skewer, brushed with oil and seasoned well. They are then cooked under a hot grill, being turned until browned on all sides. The heat is then lowered and they are cooked more slowly until tender. It is necessary to keep turning the skewers so that the meat cooks evenly. A sheet of aluminium foil in the grill pan will collect the juices which escape during cooking. Kebabs may also be baked in an oven or fried.

Various other meats are sometimes threaded on the skewer with the lamb, e.g. half kidneys, rolls of bacon, or small sausages. Fruit and vegetables can also be added, e.g. sliced tomato, sliced apple, prunes, or parboiled onions. Having made a selection, season the meats with salt, dry curry powder, and ground ginger, or merely with salt and pepper. If spices are used, they should be rubbed into the surface of the meat and it should stand for at least an hour before cooking in order to allow the flavour to penetrate the meat.

A piquant sauce should be served with kebabs. If tomato slices are put on the skewer or if curry powder is rubbed into the meat a tomato or curry sauce can accompany them.

LIVER À LA FRANÇAISE

INGREDIENTS

1 lb. calves' liver	Gravy browning
½ pt stock	1 teasp. mushroom ketchup
2 teasps. arrowroot or	or a few drops of
cornflour	Worcester sauce
4 oz. streaky bacon rashers	Parsley

FORCEMEAT

3 oz. breadcrumbs	Egg and stock to bind
¼ teasp. mixed dried herbs	½ onion or 1 shallot

METHOD

Skin and wash the liver, cut it into half-inch slices and dry them. Chop the onion or shallot until extremely fine or it will not be completely cooked when it is served. Mix the crumbs, onion, herbs, parsley and seasoning, and bind with equal parts of egg and stock. Do not make it wet, it should just hold together. Spread some of this mixture on each slice of liver. Cut the rinds from the bacon rashers and cover the forcemeat with bacon. Grease a baking tin and lay the liver in it. Pour a little stock into the tin and lay a sheet of greased paper on top of the bacon. Bake in a moderate oven (375°) until tender (30–40 minutes). If the bacon is required crisp, remove the paper about 10 minutes before the liver is done, or crisp quickly under a hot grill before serving.

Lift the liver on to a hot serving dish. Blend the arrowroot with a little cold stock and add to the liquid in the baking tin. Stir until boiling, adding extra stock if there is not enough in the tin. Correct the seasoning, add gravy browning and the ketchup or Worcestershire sauce. Strain this over the liver and garnish with parsley.

MEAT MOULD IN ASPIC

For this dish any cooked meat can be used. It should be tender and well-flavoured and not dry and insipid. Sweetbreads, tongue, chicken, rabbit, or a mixture of meats can be used, as can beef, lamb, or veal.

To make the jelly, aspic jelly crystals or gelatine are added to a well-flavoured stock. Half an ounce of gelatine will set one pint of stock; aspic crystals should be used according to the directions on the packet. If boned chicken is to be used for the mould, use the stock in which it was cooked. The stock must be clear and free from grease. Strain through a fine cloth and, preferably, allow it to get cold and lift the solid fat from the top. It must also be highly seasoned or it will taste insipid when cold.

Use skinned, sliced tomatoes or cooked green peas or mushrooms, cooked diced carrots or other brightly coloured foods to line the bottom of the mould. Allow the jelly to get cold and pour a layer of it over the vegetables and leave in a cold place to set. Fill the mould with slices or cubes of meat and add to it enough cold aspic to cover the meat. Leave to set. Turn out of the mould and serve on a bed of salad.

SWEETBREAD MOULD

Sweetbread mould can be served as follows: Chop four ounces of cooked sweetbreads very finely and stir in a quarter pint of good white sauce (fairly thick) or of cream or a mixture of the two. Season very well and stir in quarter of a pint of stock in which a quarter ounce of gelatine has been dissolved. Place into a decorated mould and leave to set. If the cream is slightly whipped the result is much lighter.

Small meat moulds set in cartons are useful for picnic meals.

MINCE OF MUTTON

Minced beef is frequently cooked, minced mutton less often. This recipe can be used for either.

INGREDIENTS

8 oz. lean mutton
¾ oz. dripping or margarine
½ teasp. very finely chopped onion
Good ¼ pt stock or water
1 rounded teasp. flour
Gravy browning
Pepper and salt
Parsley

METHOD

It is better to choose suitable meat and mince it at home;

minced meat from the butcher may contain gristle, or be of inferior quality.

Wipe the meat and trim off all fat and gristle. Pass it through a mincer or cut it into fine dice. Melt the fat in a pan and fry the onion slowly until it is clear. Add the meat and stir it in the fat until it is slightly brown. Stir in the flour and cook until a golden colour. Gradually work in the stock and add seasoning; stir until boiling. Cover with a lid and simmer slowly until tender. The time taken will depend on the quality of meat used. Tender mutton will be done in 30 minutes, less tender beef may take 1 hour. Add gravy browning if desired and serve on a hot dish with parsley to garnish.

NAVARIN OF LAMB

This is a version of navarin to be used in the early summer when young vegetables are in season.

INGREDIENTS

2 lb. shoulder, neck, or breast of lamb	1 clove garlic
1 oz. dripping, butter, or margarine	A sprig of rosemary and a bay leaf
2 medium-size onions	6 oz. tomatoes or 2 oz. purée
1 pt brown stock	5 oz. young carrots
1 oz. flour	5 oz. young turnips
Salt and pepper	4 oz. French beans
	4 oz. green peas

Breast of lamb is a very fat cut and is not very economical for this dish as most of the fat must be trimmed off. The trimmings can, of course, be heated in a slow oven to melt and produce dripping.

METHOD

Trim the meat and cut into squares. Slice the onions. Melt the dripping in a pan and fry the onions until they are clear. Add the meat and sear it on all sides. Remove the meat and onions and keep them warm while the flour is fried to a light brown colour, stirring all the time. Remove from the heat and gradually add the stock. Return to the stove and stir until boiling. Replace the meat and onions, add seasoning, herbs, and a crushed clove of garlic (the latter two tied in muslin). Skin the tomatoes, remove and discard the seeds, and chop the flesh. Add these to the pan, cover with the lid, and cook for 1 hour on top of the stove or in a slow oven (325°–340°).

Prepare the young vegetables according to their kind. Leave the carrots and turnips whole if they are very small, otherwise cut them into pieces. Cut the French beans into small diamond shapes. Put the vegetables into the stew and continue to cook it for another 45 minutes. If the peas are very young and fresh they need not be put in until about 20 minutes before the navarin is served.

Serve the navarin on a very hot dish with new potatoes.

SALMI OF GAME

A salmi is made with lightly roasted game heated in a highly seasoned wine sauce. Ideally, it is prepared at the table over a spirit lamp. Duck, wild duck, partridge, pheasant, grouse, and other game birds may be used.

The bird is roasted for half or more than half the time required to cook it to completeness and is then skinned and cut into neat joints. The carcass is broken up and pounded to release the juice in it. The neck and liver can also be used to give flavour to the sauce. The carcass, neck, and liver are heated in a pan with Espagnole sauce, wine, shallots, and

seasoning, where they simmer until the volume is reduced.
Fat is skimmed off the top and the sauce is strained over the
joints of game.

The joints are either simmered in sauce until tender, or
they are kept warm in a covered pan while the sauce is
prepared so that further cooking is unnecessary. Mushrooms
and Madeira wine are often added just before serving.

There are many recipes for salmi, some of which include
redcurrant jelly, spices, lemon juice, and tomato purée, but a
classic preparation of salmi of pheasant can be prepared as
follows:

INGREDIENTS

1 *moderately done roasted*
  pheasant
½ *bottle red wine*
1 *oz. chopped shallots*
¼ *pt Espagnole sauce*
  (preferably made with
  game stock)

Freshly milled pepper
6 *button mushrooms, cooked*
  in ¼ *oz. butter and* 1
  teasp. lemon juice in a
  covered pan – reserve the
  liquor

METHOD

Cut the bird into portions and remove the skin. Place the
cooked flesh into a thick pan with the juice from the roasting
tin (juice only and *not* fat) and keep covered and warm. A
few drops of brandy added to this improves the dish.

Crush the carcass and place it together with the neck,
liver, and skin in a pan with the chopped shallots, wine, and
some pepper. Cook rapidly to reduce the wine by more than
half its volume. Add the Espagnole sauce and cook for at
least 5 minutes. Strain into a clean pan and add the liquid
from the mushroom pan and from the joints of pheasant
and reduce the whole to half its volume. Correct the seasoning. Place the joints in a hot serving dish, add the mushrooms, and strain the sauce over them.

SAVOURY HAM

INGREDIENTS

½ oz. butter
1 slice gammon, ½ in. thick
  and weighing 12 to 14 oz.
8 oz. tomatoes
¼ onion or 1 small shallot

1 teasp. chopped parsley
1 oz. breadcrumbs
6 mushrooms
Parsley sprigs

METHOD

Wipe the ham and place in a frying-pan. Cover with cold water and bring gently to the boil. Pour off the water and put the butter into the frying-pan. Fry the mushrooms and the ham very slowly on both sides until done (about 10–15 minutes). Lift out and keep hot. Fry the onion slowly in the fat in the pan until it is quite clear. Skin and slice the tomatoes and add these to the onion. Cook for a few moments. Add sufficient breadcrumbs to absorb most of the liquid in the pan and then stir in the chopped parsley and seasoning. Pile this on the ham and garnish with fried mushrooms and parsley sprigs.

Stalks from the mushrooms can be chopped finely and cooked with the onion for the stuffing.

SWEETBREADS

Veal sweetbreads are a delicacy and can be cooked by braising, poaching, grilling, stewing, or frying. They can also be cooked and set in aspic to serve cold with salad.

Two glands are sold as sweetbreads. One is the thymus or 'throatbread' which is a long shape. This is less of a delicacy than the other, the pancreas or 'heartbread', which is more round in shape.

It is necessary to blanch sweetbreads before use. Wash them first in salted water and then put into a pan and cover with cold water. Bring the water slowly to the boil, simmer for 10 minutes, and then strain. Throw away the water and cover the sweetbreads with cold water. When they are cold, remove any inedible material and lay them between two plates with a small weight on top so that the meat is flattened.

BRAISED SWEETBREAD

METHOD

Use the recipe for braised meat but modify it as follows:

Cut the vegetables into a julienne and include celery. Do not fry the vegetables before putting them into the braising pot. Cook the sweetbreads about 1¼ hours, or until tender. Baste frequently while cooking to glaze the surface of the meat. Serve the sweetbreads with a Julienne of vegetables at each end of the dish.

FRIED SWEETBREADS

Cut the blanched sweetbreads into slices and season well. Heat some butter in a pan and cook the slices gently on both sides without browning. When done, arrange neatly in a pile on a hot dish and coat with Mornay sauce. Sprinkle with grated cheese and brown under a grill. Garnish with cooked asparagus tips.

GRILLED SWEETBREADS

Grilled sweetbreads can be served with mushrooms and grilled bacon. Cut blanched sweetbreads into thick slices and brush with melted fat. Sear for 2 minutes on each side, lower the heat, and continue to turn them frequently until they are done.

STEWED SWEETBREADS

INGREDIENTS

2 sweetbreads (blanched and
   pressed)
¾ pt milk
1 small carrot
½ small turnip
1 small onion
Bouquet garni

Pepper and salt
1 oz. butter
1 oz. flour
1 tablesp. cream
Parsley
Small shapes cut from sliced
   cooked tongue or ham

METHOD

Put the sweetbreads in a pan and add half a pint of milk, the
bouquet garni, pepper, and vegetables cut into small pieces.
Bring to the boil, lower the heat, and simmer gently until
tender (about 1 hour). Blend the flour with the remaining
quarter-pint of milk, add to the stew, and stir until boiling.
Add butter, season with salt, remove the bouquet garni, and
then stir in a tablespoon of cream. Place the sweetbreads on
a dish and strain the sauce over them. Garnish with parsley
and small shapes cut from thin slices of cooked ham or
tongue.

TÊTE DE VEAU

A calf's head is more popular in France than in England,
but it is a dish which is much esteemed by those who eat
it.

INGREDIENTS

Half a calf's head
Lemon
Onion, carrot, turnip, and
   celery to flavour the stock

Bouquet garni plus two
   cloves
Salt and 12 peppercorns
Parsley sauce
Parsley sprigs

METHOD

Trim and wash the head well in cold water and remove the
brains. Place it in a pan of cold water, bring to the boil and
simmer for 30 minutes. Pour away the water and plunge
the head into cold water. Then rub it all over with a cut
lemon to prevent it darkening. Return to the clean pan, and
cover with water and the rest of the juice from the lemon.
Add the vegetables cut up coarsely, some salt, the peppercorns, and a bouquet garni. Bring to the boil and then lower
the heat. Simmer gently until tender – about 2½–3 hours.
Remove the tongue and the bones and roll up the head and
secure with a skewer before serving. Alternatively, cut the
meat into large cubes. Lay the meat on a dish and garnish
with parsley sprigs, tongue, and brains. Serve parsley sauce
separately. Make this sauce with equal parts of milk and
stock from the cooking pot.

The brains should be washed, blanched, tied in muslin, and
cooked with the head for the last half-hour. The tongue
should be skinned and sliced before serving.

An alternative sauce to serve with calf's head is a vinaigrette to which has been added finely chopped onion, tarragon, chervil, and gherkins and also a little of the cooked
brains previously pressed through a hair sieve.

TRIPE AND ONIONS

INGREDIENTS

1 lb. dressed tripe	¼ oz. flour
4 oz. onions	½ oz. butter
½ pt milk or milk and water mixed	Pepper and salt
	Parsley

METHOD

Wipe the tripe and cut it into neat pieces. Peel and slice the onions. Put the tripe, onions, and milk in a pan and bring to the boil.

Lower the heat and simmer slowly until tender (about 1 hour). Beat together the butter and flour and drop a small piece at a time into the pan, stirring constantly. When the sauce is smooth, correct the seasoning and pour the stew into a hot serving dish. Garnish with parsley and triangles of toasted bread. A little grated nutmeg can be added to the sauce.

TRIPE FRIED

INGREDIENTS

1 lb. cooked tripe	Pepper and salt
Egg	1 onion
Breadcrumbs	Parsley

METHOD

Peel the onion and slice across into paper-thin slices and separate each slice into rings.

Wash and dry the tripe and cut it into fairly small pieces. Season with pepper and salt. Dip into beaten egg and then into breadcrumbs. Fry in hot, deep fat until golden brown, and drain on kitchen paper. Dip each onion ring into milk and then into flour, and fry in the hot fat until brown. Drain on paper.

Place the tripe on a dish mat on a hot serving dish and sprinkle the onion rings on top. Garnish with parsley.

VIENNA STEAKS

These can be made with fillet steak but can also be prepared less expensively by using top rump or another cut of similar quality.

INGREDIENTS

½ lb. beef	Breadcrumbs
2 oz. beef marrow	½ an egg yolk
1 oz. onion – chopped finely	Butter for frying
1 tablesp. parsley – chopped finely	4 fried eggs
Salt, pepper, and grated nutmeg	Parsley
	Onion rings fried in fat (see Fried Tripe)

METHOD

Cook the onion gently, until clear, in a small pan. Use a little butter for frying and keep the lid on the pan.

Chop or mince the meat and bone marrow. Add the cooked onion, chopped parsley, seasonings, and egg yolk. Mix thoroughly and divide the mixture into four equal portions. Shape into flat, round cakes and dust lightly with breadcrumbs.

Heat a little butter in a frying-pan and cook the steaks on one side until half done. Turn them and finish cooking them without further turning. Lift on to a serving dish and keep hot. Put a little more butter into the pan and heat until it is nut-brown. Pour this over the steaks. Put a fried egg on each steak and garnish with fried onion rings and parsley.

A thin gravy is served with Vienna steaks.

CHAPTER 4

Cheese

SEVERAL cheese dishes will be found in other parts of this book. For example, the recipe for 'Cheese and Celery bars' is given under *Savouries* and that for 'Cheese omelet' under *Supper dishes*.

Many everyday cheese dishes have a great deal of starchy food with them; for example, Macaroni Cheese and Welsh Rarebit. Recipes for these dishes have either been left out, or alternatives suggested. Welsh Rarebit appears served on a bed of spinach instead of the usual toast.

Many cheeses can be cooked without added salt. It is, however, usual to add cayenne pepper, mustard, nutmeg, or even Worcestershire sauce to cooked cheese dishes. The flavour and digestibility are both improved by adequate seasoning. On the whole, a well-flavoured imported hard cheese is best for cooked dishes. English regional cheeses are ideal for a cheeseboard.

*

CHEESE AND TOMATO HOTPOT

This requires a cheese with a good flavour.

INGREDIENTS

1 lb. tomatoes	½ pt milk
6–8 oz. grated cheese	Salt and pepper
2 eggs	2 oz. breadcrumbs

METHOD

Skin the tomatoes and cut into halves or thick slices. Put a layer of tomatoes on the bottom of a greased dish and season well. Sprinkle with crumbs and grated cheese. Repeat until the tomatoes and cheese are used up. Beat the eggs, add seasoning, and stir in the milk. Strain over the cheese mixture. Bake in a moderate oven (350°) for about 30 minutes or until the custard is set.

Cooking apples can be used in place of tomatoes and a teaspoonful of made mustard can be added to the eggs.

CHEESE AND PINEAPPLE KEBABS

These are a refreshing addition to a picnic or buffet meal.

Dice canned pineapple and processed cheese neatly and impale one cube of each on a cocktail stick. If the cubes are small enough, more than two can be accommodated on one stick.

CHEESE DIP

A sour milk cheese diluted with mayonnaise makes an appetizing dip for cocktail parties or out-of-door meals. Add home-made mayonnaise gradually, beating well all the time, until the mixture is smooth and of a coating consistency. Add seasoning, and flavour if you wish with tomato purée or chopped fresh herbs. Dip into this raw cauliflower sprigs or pieces of cucumber impaled on cocktail sticks. Pineapple cubes or short lengths of banana are equally pleasant. Banana should be brushed with lemon juice to prevent it turning black when it is exposed to the air.

CHEESE STICKS

Take a firm cheese such as cheddar and cut into fingers about two to two and a half inches long and half an inch across. Spread with a little made mustard, dip into beaten egg and then into breadcrumbs and fry in hot deep fat until golden. Drain well on paper, serve on a dish mat, and sprinkle with a little grated cheese and chopped parsley.

CHEESE SOUFFLÉ

INGREDIENTS

2 oz. butter	4 eggs
1½ oz. flour	Salt
½ pt milk	Cayenne pepper
4 oz. Gruyère cheese, or	Grated nutmeg
6 oz. Cheddar	Watercress

METHOD

Separate the egg whites and yolks. Grate the cheese. Melt the butter in a fairly large pan, stir in the flour and seasonings and gradually work in the milk. Stir until boiling, cool slightly, and pour a little of the hot sauce on to the beaten egg yolks. Stir well and return to the pan and mix thoroughly. Add the grated cheese and correct the seasoning. Beat the egg whites until they do not flow if the bowl is inverted, and fold this foam very carefully into the cheese mixture in the pan. Transfer the mixture to a prepared soufflé case and bake just above the centre of the oven at 425° until well risen and set. A skewer inserted in the centre will come out clean when the mixture is cooked.

Remove the paper from the soufflé case and stand it on a dish covered with a dish mat. Garnish with bunches of watercress and serve very hot.

PREPARATION OF SOUFFLÉ CASE

Fold a double strip of greaseproof paper or aluminium foil round the soufflé case so that it projects two inches above the rim. Tie securely into position. Grease inside the dish and the paper very thoroughly.

COLD CHEESE SOUFFLÉ

INGREDIENTS

3 oz. imported Cheddar
   cheese (strong)
2 tablesps. cold white sauce

Cayenne pepper and
   mustard
¼ pt aspic jelly
Radish and watercress

METHOD

Prepare a soufflé case (see previous recipe) but do not grease, and make the aspic jelly according to the directions on the packet. Grate the cheese very finely indeed and stir into the sauce. Allow the aspic jelly to get quite cold but not set. Whisk it until it is spongy and shows signs of setting and then whisk in the cheese mixture a teaspoonful at a time. Pour into the soufflé case and chill in the refrigerator. Decorate the top with small blanched leaves of watercress and thin slices of radish. Spoon a little cold aspic jelly over the top and chill in the refrigerator so that the surface is brilliant. Remove the paper from the soufflé case by running a hot knife blade round the outside.

CHICORY WITH CHEESE SAUCE

Wash and trim three-quarters to one pound of chicory. Tie together in small bundles with string and place into cold, salted water with a little lemon juice in it. Bring to the boil and pour off the water. This removes much of the bitter flavour. Plunge into fast boiling salted water with lemon juice in and boil till the vegetable is done. Drain thoroughly in a colander. Make half a pint of cheese sauce, spread a little on the bottom of a hot fireproof dish, and lay the chicory neatly on it. Coat with the remaining sauce. Sprinkle a little grated cheese over the surface and brown under a hot grill. Garnish with parsley.

Practically any vegetable or mixture of vegetables can be served this way, although green leaves are not satisfactory.

CHICORY MILANAISE

Wash and trim three-quarters of a pound of chicory and place in heavy pan with one ounce of butter and a teaspoonful lemon juice, salt and about two tablespoonfuls of cold water. Cover the vegetables closely with a sheet of greased paper and put a lid on the pan. Cook over a slow flame until tender. This will take 20 minutes or more. Be careful not to let the pan boil dry. When the vegetable is done, transfer it to a hot fireproof dish, sprinkle the surface generously with grated cheese, and heat half to one ounce of butter until nut-brown and pour it over the chicory. Brown quickly under a hot grill. Garnish with parsley.

Other vegetables can be cooked this way; sea-kale, for example, is excellent. Parsnips can be finished in the same way but should be cooked until tender in boiling salted water. Because they are boiled and not cooked in the lemon juice the dish is called gratinated parsnips.

FONDUE

Fondue is served in the earthenware pan in which it is cooked. It is usual to impale a square of bread or toast on the end of the fork and dip it into the fondue. You can, of course, use starch-reduced rolls cut into small pieces. Everyone dips into the same pan of fondue.

There are various recipes for fondue, some with eggs and some without. Good Swiss cheese must be used. Gruyère is usually recommended, but it can be mixed with Tilsiter or Emmenthal or both.

INGREDIENTS

1 *clove garlic*	1 *lb. Gruyère cheese*
¼ *pt white wine*	1 *tablesp. Kirsch*

METHOD

Crush the garlic and rub it on the bottom of the casserole.
Grate the cheese and mix it with the wine. Place over a very
low heat and stir constantly until the whole becomes smooth
and creamy. Stir the Kirsch in last. A good pinch of cornflour or potato flour can be mixed with the Kirsch. If the
mixture becomes stringy as it is stirred, do not worry;
it will become smooth with further gentle heating and
stirring.

The second recipe contains eggs.

INGREDIENTS

1 *clove garlic*	4 *oz. grated Gruyère (or*
¼ *pt white wine*	*mixed cheeses)*
6 *eggs*	*Black pepper and salt*
2 *oz. butter*	

METHOD

Put the wine and the garlic (crushed and chopped) into a
pan and cook until the volume is reduced by half. Strain
and cool. Beat the eggs in a bowl and add a generous amount
of salt, pepper, and the reduced wine. Transfer to an earthenware dish, stir in the grated cheese and the butter, previously
cut into small pieces. Continue to stir over a very low flame
until the mixture is creamy. Do not overheat or the eggs will
become scrambled, and do not stop stirring or the same thing
may happen on the bottom of the pan.

This recipe can be made with half the quantity of wine;
in this case the volume is not reduced over a flame. Either
warm the wine with the crushed garlic in it and strain off the

garlic before use, or rub the crushed garlic round the inside of the cooking dish. M. Boulestin makes fondue with these proportions of cheese, eggs, and butter but does not use wine or garlic.

LORRAINE EGGS

INGREDIENTS

Gruyère cheese	*Butter*
Bacon rashers	*Parsley*
Eggs	

METHOD

Cut the cheese in very thin slices. Butter a fireproof dish and lay the cheese on the bottom. Remove the bacon rinds and fry the rashers until crisp. Lay these on the cheese. Spread the eggs over the bacon, put small pieces of butter on the egg yolks and bake in a moderate oven (375°) until the eggs are cooked to your taste. Garnish with parsley or cooked mushrooms with their cups sprinkled with chopped parsley.

The quantities in this recipe are left to the discretion of the cook. Seasoning this dish is difficult because pepper gives a speckled appearance to the baked eggs. It is probably best to omit it entirely.

PARMESAN EGGS

INGREDIENTS

4 oz. chopped onion	*2–3 oz. grated Parmesan*
1 oz. butter	*cheese*
1 oz. flour	*Salt and pepper*
½ pt milk	*Parsley*
Hard-boiled eggs	

METHOD

Fry the onion gently in butter until clear and then raise the heat to brown it a little. Sprinkle the flour over the onions and stir until it is slightly coloured. Gradually work in the milk and stir until boiling. Season to taste.

Grease a fireproof dish and place slices or halves of hard-boiled eggs in the dish. Coat with the onion sauce and sprinkle the surface with grated Parmesan cheese and a few small pieces of butter or margarine. Heat through at the top of a hot oven just long enough to brown the surface and heat the eggs. Garnish with parsley.

Parmesan is expensive but gives a delicious flavour to the dish. A cheaper cheese can, of course, be used.

ROES IN CHEESE SAUCE

INGREDIENTS

½ lb. soft herring roes	Fat for frying
½ pt cheese sauce	Flour
1 oz. grated cheese	Pepper and salt
Chopped parsley	

METHOD

Wash and dry the roes. Add pepper and salt to some flour and dip the roes into the mixture. Shake off the surplus flour. Heat a little fat in a frying-pan and cook the roes very lightly. Drain on paper. Transfer them to a greased baking dish and pour the cheese sauce over them. Sprinkle with grated cheese and brown under a hot grill. Sprinkle with chopped parsley before serving.

STUFFED MARROW

INGREDIENTS

1 small marrow	1 tablesp. chopped parsley
8 oz. processed cheese cut into very tiny cubes	1 tablesp. breadcrumbs
	Pepper and salt

3 oz. streaky bacon cut into
small pieces and fried
2 oz. mushrooms chopped
finely

1 teasp. made mustard
(optional)
Dripping
Parsley

METHOD

Peel the marrow and shave a small piece off one side so that
it will lie steadily. Cut an oval shape from the opposite side
and scoop out the seeds through the hole thus made.

Put the marrow into fast-boiling salted water and cook
for 5 minutes. Drain well and cool. Mix the cheese, bacon,
mushrooms, parsley, crumbs, and seasoning and pack into
the marrow. Replace the oval piece previously cut out. Place
into a baking dish containing some hot dripping and baste
well. Cover with a sheet of greased paper and bake in a
moderate oven (375°) for 30–40 minutes. Baste frequently
while cooking. Lift on to paper to drain off surplus grease
and then serve on a hot dish with parsley as a garnish. Serve
with a cheese sauce.

A little chopped fried onion or chopped raw tomato and
even diced cooked vegetables can be added to this stuffing.

STUFFED PEPPERS

INGREDIENTS

Green or red peppers (the
number required depends
on their size)
Butter
4 oz. cooked meat
2 oz. grated cheese
4 oz. tomato

1 shallot
½ lb. cooked French beans
(cut into small pieces), or
½ lb. cooked peas
1 oz. breadcrumbs
Pepper and salt
Chopped parsley

METHOD

Cut the peppers in halves lengthwise and remove the seeds.

Peel and chop the tomatoes, discarding the seeds. Chop the meat. Chop the shallots very finely. Mix the meat, cheese, tomato, shallots and beans or peas, and season well. Fill the peppers with this mixture. Sprinkle breadcrumbs over the top and put small pats of butter on the crumbs. Place into a baking dish and pour boiling water into the dish until it comes half-way up the peppers. Lay a sheet of greased paper on top and bake in a moderate oven (375°) until the peppers are tender. Drain well, sprinkle with chopped parsley, and serve on a hot dish.

The shallots can be cooked gently in half an ounce of butter before mixing with the rest of the stuffing, to ensure they are completely done and mild in flavour.

SWISS PIE

This dish is normally baked on a pastry shell but the cheese mixture can be baked in a pie dish. Cream is used to make this recipe, but it can, of course, be replaced partly or wholly by milk. The result will, however, not be so delectable.

INGREDIENTS

2 oz. Swiss cheese, diced very small

2 oz. mushrooms, sliced

2 rashers of bacon, cut into small strips

2 tablesps. chopped parsley

The juice of one small onion

¼ teasp. grated nutmeg

Freshly milled pepper

Salt

4 eggs

¾ pt cream

½ oz. butter or margarine

METHOD

Melt the fat in a small pan and cook the sliced mushrooms in it for 3 minutes. Add the bacon and fry lightly. Remove from the stove and add the onion juice, nutmeg, pepper, cheese, and parsley, and mix together very thoroughly.

Sprinkle this mixture on the bottom of a greased baking dish. Beat the eggs and add the cream and seasoning. Strain this mixture into a baking dish. Place the baking dish in a deep tin containing enough water to come nearly to the top. Cook in a slow oven (325°) until the custard is set. This will take 35–40 minutes.

A little chopped fresh tarragon can be added to this dish; this gives a distinctive flavour, but it should be used with discretion.

WELSH RAREBIT ON SPINACH

INGREDIENTS

1½ oz. grated cheese
1 teasp. cornflour
1 tablesp. milk
Salt

Cayenne pepper and
   mustard
Parsley

METHOD

Mix the cheese, cornflour, and seasoning with milk to give a fairly stiff paste. It may be necessary to add a little extra milk to some cheeses. Place a neat block of cooked spinach on a small fireproof dish and cover completely with the cheese mixture. Place under a very hot grill and cook until brown. Garnish with parsley.

BUCK RAREBIT

Buck rarebit is Welsh rarebit with a poached egg on top.

Beer is frequently used in place of milk in Welsh or Buck rarebit.

CHAPTER 5

Savouries

AFTER-DINNER savouries are highly seasoned and so
stimulate the flow of digestive juices. A very small selection
is given here, some of which are normally served on croûtons
of fried or toasted bread. This, of course, need not be eaten.

*

ANGELS ON HORSEBACK

INGREDIENTS

6 cooking oysters
6 thin rashers bacon
6 thin circles fried bread

Lemon slices
Chopped parsley

METHOD

Remove the rind from the bacon and flatten each rasher
with a knife blade. Roll one rasher of bacon round each
oyster and secure with a stainless steel skewer. Cook under a
hot grill, turning frequently until done. Serve each roll on
a small circle of fried bread. Dust with chopped parsley and
serve with lemon slices.

ASPIC MOULDS

A selection from the following:

Prawns, shrimps, diced
   shellfish, diced chicken,
   sliced hard-boiled eggs

Walnuts
Aspic jelly
Watercress

Cooked peas   Lettuce
Diced cooked carrots   Tomato

METHOD

Dissolve the aspic crystals in water or preferably in a clear, well-flavoured stock. Season generously and leave to get quite cold. (Before use the stock should be strained through a fine cloth so that there are no solid particles in it, and left to get cold so that all grease can be lifted from the top.)

Take small metal moulds or darioles and pour a very thin layer of aspic into each. Arrange on this a ring of cooked peas or a decoration made from blanched watercress leaves or other strongly coloured vegetables. Leave to set and then pour in a second thin layer of aspic to hold the decoration in position. Leave again to set. Dice the chosen meat or fish and remove any fat or gristle from the meat. Place a layer in each mould, cover with cold jelly, and leave to set. Then place a layer of cooked peas or carrots on the jelly, cover with more aspic, and leave to set. Continue with alternate layers of flesh and vegetables until the mould is full. When it is to be used, dip quickly into hot water and turn each mould out on to a serving plate. Garnish with small leaves of watercress and lettuce and with tomato slices.

The selection of foods used in one mould is a matter of personal choice. Slices of hard-boiled egg are frequently pressed against the side of the mould to give a good appearance when it is served. The cavity in the centre can be filled with shrimps or vegetables. Chopped egg does not look well and should be avoided.

A refreshing mould can be made with prawns, walnuts, and grapefruit segments, using grapefruit juice to dilute the aspic crystals. If canned juice is too sweet, lemon juice can be added to it.

CHEESE AND CELERY BARS

Any soft cheese such as sour milk or cream cheese or Demi-sel can be used.

INGREDIENTS

Soft cheese
Celery

Paprika pepper
Chopped parsley

METHOD

Cut two-inch lengths of the white central stalks of celery and wash them clean. Shave a little from the curved side so that each piece will lie firmly on a serving dish with the hollow side uppermost. Fill the cavity of the stalk with cheese, either piling it in with a fork or piping it in. Decorate with small celery leaves, red pepper, and chopped parsley.

If the cheese is too stiff for piping add a little cream or top milk. Seasoning can be added to taste. Grated hard cheese mixed with lightly whipped cream can be used in place of a soft cheese.

CREAM CHEESE WALNUTS

INGREDIENTS

1 Demisel cheese or ¼ lb.
  cream cheese
1 teasp. chopped parsley
1 teasp. chopped capers,
  gherkins and olives
  mixed

Cayenne pepper and salt
Walnuts
Chopped parsley
Paprika pepper
Small cress

METHOD

Mix the cheese and chopped vegetables together and season well. Roll into very small balls and sandwich each one between two halves of shelled walnut. Place a line of chopped parsley along the top of one savoury and a line of paprika along the next. Continue until they are all decorated, using a knife blade to lift and place the decoration. Put each cream cheese walnut into a paper sweet case and serve on a dish with small cress as a garnish.

DEVILLED ROES

INGREDIENTS

Soft herring roes	1 tablesp. oil
1 teasp. dry mustard	Cayenne pepper and salt
1 teasp. Worcestershire sauce	Lemon juice
Anchovy essence	Parsley

METHOD

Wash and dry the roes. Moisten the mustard with anchovy essence, stir the Worcestershire sauce into it, and blend until smooth. Leave to stand for 30 minutes and then add the oil and a few drops of lemon juice. Season with salt and cayenne pepper.

Grease a shallow fireproof dish and lay the roes in it. Brush with the devilled sauce and grill for a few minutes. Turn carefully, brush the other side with devilled sauce, and return to the grill until cooked. Serve on buttered toast. Garnish with parsley.

DEVILS ON HORSEBACK

INGREDIENTS

6 Jordan almonds	Oil
6 large prunes	Salt and cayenne pepper
6 circles fried or toasted bread	Chopped parsley
6 thin rashers bacon	

METHOD

Put the prunes into boiling water and soak overnight. Fry the almonds in oil until golden brown, drain on paper, and season with salt and cayenne pepper. Remove the rind from the bacon and flatten each rasher with a knife blade. Remove the stones from the prunes and replace each stone by a fried almond. Roll a rasher round each prune and secure with a stainless steel skewer. Grill until the bacon is cooked, turning frequently. Serve each one on a circle of fried or toasted bread and sprinkle with chopped parsley.

ROGNONS NORGES

INGREDIENTS

1 sheep's kidney
¾ oz. butter
1 teasp. chopped parsley
1 chopped olive }
1 chopped gherkin } Optional

1 teasp. flour
Pepper and salt
Bacon rashers
Egg and breadcrumbs
Chopped parsley

METHOD

Skin and wash the kidney, remove the core, and chop the rest finely. Melt the butter in a small pan, add the kidney and cook gently for 15 minutes with a lid on. Sprinkle the flour over the kidney and stir until it is golden. Add olive, gherkin, parsley, and seasoning. Spread this mixture on a plate and leave to become cold. Cut the rind from the bacon, flatten each rasher with a knife and cut into lengths of about two to two and a half inches. Place a teaspoonful of kidney mixture on each piece of bacon, and roll up. Dip into egg and then into breadcrumbs. Fry in the hot deep fat until well browned. Drain on paper and then serve each rognon in a paper case. Dust with chopped parsley.

SCOTCH WOODCOCK

INGREDIENTS

2 eggs
9 anchovies
¾ oz. butter
3 tablesps. cream or milk
Pepper

Parsley
Buttered toast cut into
   fingers and with crusts
   removed

METHOD

Reserve two anchovy fillets for garnishing and chop the rest.
Beat the egg and add pepper. Place the butter in a small pan
and melt it. Add the egg and cream and stir over a slow
heat until it begins to thicken. Stir in the chopped anchovies
and continue to cook until the egg is firm. Pile on to fingers
of buttered toast. Garnish with small strips of anchovy
fillet and with parsley.

STUFFED MUSHROOMS

INGREDIENTS

6 medium sized mushrooms
¼ oz. butter
½ teasp. very finely
   chopped onion
2 teasps. chopped ham
1 teasp. chopped parsley

1 dessertsp. breadcrumbs, or
   1 tablesp. well-flavoured
   sauce
6 small circles fried bread
Pepper and salt
Paprika pepper

METHOD

Skin and wash the mushrooms. If they are not all the same
size, trim them with a pastry cutter. Chop the stalks and
trimmings. Melt the butter in a small pan and fry the onion
gently until clear. Add the mushroom trimmings and ham,

and cook until tender. Add seasoning and parsley and bind together with sauce or breadcrumbs.

Grease a baking tray and put the mushrooms in it hollow side uppermost. Fill each mushroom with stuffing, cover with greased paper, and bake at 375° until the mushrooms are tender – 10–15 minutes. Serve each one on a bread croûte and garnish with paprika pepper.

STUFFED PRUNES

INGREDIENTS

6 prunes
6 small plain biscuits about
   1-in. in diameter
2 tablesps. water
2 tablesps. sherry
1½ oz. butter or margarine

2 teasps. anchovy essence
Worcestershire sauce
Lemon juice
Cayenne pepper
Watercress

METHOD

Soak the prunes in sherry and water until tender, or cook gently until soft. Cream the butter in a small basin until very pale. Gradually beat in the anchovy essence and enough sauce and lemon juice to give a very sharp flavour. Season well. Slit each prune down one side and carefully remove the stones. Fill the cavity with some of the savoury butter and spread a little on each biscuit. Place one prune on each biscuit. Put the remaining butter in a piping bag and pipe small stars all round the edge of the biscuit and across the cut in the prune. Garnish with watercress.

CHAPTER 6

Supper Dishes

THESE are recipes suitable for supper time, and supplement those given in other sections which may be equally suitable.

*

BACON, EGG, AND BANANA

Since there is no recipe elsewhere in this book for fried egg and since some amateur cooks may look for it, here it is.

The secret of the successfully fried egg lies simply in the temperature of the fat. If this is too high the edges of the white will become brown and hard. On the other hand, if the fat is too cool the white will spread over the pan. Experience and a steady flame will show when to put in the egg. It is a job which calls for two hands – one to hold the handle of the pan so that it can be lifted off the stove or tipped to one side to prevent the white spreading too far. For this reason, do not try to break the egg shell on the side of the pan. Break the egg into a small basin first and then pour it gently into the hot fat. Bacon fat is frequently used for frying eggs, and if the yolk of the egg is to be basted with fat it is important that there are no solid pieces in the fat or the surface of the yolk will have a speckled appearance.

Cut the rind off bacon rashers and make several cuts into the fat part, using scissors or a knife. This prevents the bacon rashers curling up as they become hot. Peel a banana and cut into halves lengthwise and then cut each half into two pieces. Melt a little fat in the pan and put in the bacon and banana. Cook very gently until they are both clear. The banana should be turned with a palate knife. When it is done, lift it on to a hot dish. Turn up the heat and crisp the bacon and then put this on the hot dish. Lower the heat, tilt the pan a little and pour in the egg. Adjust the heat at once if necessary and cook the egg gently until the white is set. Baste the yolk with bacon fat if desired. Lift it on to the hot dish and serve.

As an alternative to banana, use quarters or thick slices of cooking apples. Remove the core from each slice.

If sausages are being fried as well you should put them into the pan first and cook very gently until well done, turning them at intervals. Some juice generally escapes from sausages and sticks to the pan. Avoid this when frying the egg or it, too, will stick to the pan.

All these foods should be fried slowly. If the heat is excessive they will burn and pieces will break off them.

BAKED EGGS: Recipe 1

For these dishes, small individual earthenware cocotte moulds are ideal. Take one mould for each egg and grease it well.

INGREDIENTS

3 eggs	3 dessertsps. milk
3 dessertsps. chopped ham or lean bacon	3 dessertsps. grated cheese
	½ oz. butter
1 teasp. chopped onion	Parsley
3 teasps. breadcrumbs	Salt and pepper

METHOD

Melt the butter in a small pan and fry the onion slowly until clear. Now add the ham and fry this too. Place this mixture on the bottom of three greased cocotte moulds. Break an egg into each one, season it and add one dessertspoon of milk and one of grated cheese. Bake in a hot oven (425°) just until the egg is set. This will require a little over 5 minutes. Serve at once with a parsley garnish.

BAKED EGGS: RECIPE 2

INGREDIENTS

3 eggs	Salt and pepper
¼ pt cheese sauce	Fresh tarragon
3 teasps. grated cheese	

METHOD

Grease three cocotte moulds. Bring a pint of water to the boil in a small pan and add a teaspoon of lemon juice. Break an egg into a small basin, stir the water to a whirlpool with a fork, and drop the egg into the centre. Draw the pan to the side of the stove and let the egg poach below boiling-point until it is cooked. Drain and put into a cocotte mould. Repeat until all the eggs are cooked.

Place a small sprig of fresh tarragon on top of each egg and coat with cheese sauce. Sprinkle with grated cheese and brown under the hot grill.

HERRINGS

Herrings are usually fried, grilled, or soused, but there are many ways of dressing them to give variety.

GRILLED HERRING

Grilled herring is usually left unsplit, but the head is taken off and the inside is cleaned under a running tap. Make two or three deep incisions in the flesh on both sides of the fish and near the backbone and brush the surface with oil. Sprinkle with seasoning. Heat the grill. Grease the grill

trivet and place the fish on it. Heat for 2 minutes on each
side under a hot grill and then lower the heat and continue
to cook on alternate sides until done. Serve with parsley
garnish.

The flavour is improved if savoury butter is added. Take a
little butter or margarine and beat it in a basin with pepper,
salt, and lemon juice. Chopped parsley or fennel can be
added. This can be pressed into the incisions in the flesh
before the fish is cooked, and any fat which falls into the
grill pan forms a sauce to serve with the fish.

Mackerel can be grilled in the same way as herring.

FRIED HERRING

Slit the fish the whole length of the underside and cut off the
head. Open the fish and put on a board with back uppermost.
Hit the back with a clenched fist all along its length. Turn
the fish over and slide the thumbs under each side of the
backbone from head to tail. This draws the bones from the
sides of the fish and enables the backbone to be pulled out
whole. Wash and dry the fish, season it with pepper, salt,
and lemon juice. Dip into flour or into oatmeal and fry in
hot fat in a frying-pan. Put the inner side of the fish downwards and turn it when brown on one side. Pieces of
browned oatmeal or flour fall off the fish and adhere to the
surface which is fried last, thus spoiling its appearance.
This is why the surface which is served uppermost is fried
first.

BAKED HERRINGS

Bone the herrings, remove their heads, wash and dry them.
Season with salt, pepper, and lemon juice and sprinkle with
chopped parsley. Roll up and wrap each one in greased
paper and put on a baking tray in a moderate oven (375°)
for about 15 minutes. Garnish with parsley and lemon. The
roes can be rolled inside the fish.

GOODWOOD HERRINGS

For every herring take:

1 *tomato*	*A pinch of chopped thyme,*
1 *dessertsp. breadcrumbs*	*or fennel, or dill*
1 *saltspoon chopped shallot*	*Pepper and salt*
A little grated lemon rind	*Butter*
1 *teasp. chopped parsley*	

METHOD

Clean and wash the herrings. Remove the eyes and break the bone between the eye-sockets. Pass the tail through this aperture and secure it with a matchstick or a cocktail stick. Put the herring on a greased baking tray. Cut a slice off one end of the tomato and scoop out the inside with a teaspoon. Invert to drain.

Mix the rest of the ingredients together and moisten with some of the tomato pulp. Fill the tomato, put a little butter on the filling, and cover with the slice which was cut off.

Put the tomato in the centre of the herring, cover with greased paper, and bake for about 20 minutes in a fairly hot oven (390°).

If this recipe is used for mackerel, fennel is the most suitable herb.

HERRING PIE

INGREDIENTS

Herrings	Butter
Apples	Ground mace, pepper, and
Onions	salt

METHOD

This pie was popular about two centuries ago when exact

quantities were not specified. Recipe books of that day
direct that the herrings be gutted, beheaded, freed from fins,
tails, and scales, washed, and dried. Grease a baking dish
and place in it the herrings, seasoned with pepper and salt
and a little mace. Over this place a layer of thinly sliced
apple and onion. Pour on a little water and cover with a
pie crust. It must be well baked to ensure that the onion is
done.

The elasticity of some old recipes is refreshing, and the
quantities of apple and onion in this pie can well be left to
personal taste or available ingredients.

There is no reason why the pastry crust should not be
omitted and the dish made in a casserole with a lid on.
Instead of baking in a hot oven as one would with a pastry
crust, it can be cooked gently for 2 hours or more. The dish
will have a better appearance if a second layer of herrings,
skin side uppermost, is laid over the apple and onion.

OMELETS

Two eggs make a generous omelet for one person. Three
eggs, however, may be enough for two people and four eggs
could serve three.

An omelet pan is a necessity in any household. It should
be of heavy steel or aluminium and there should be a wide
curve from the base to the rim. A sharp angle between base
and sides, as in a frying-pan, makes it difficult to turn out
an omelet. The pan should never be washed. This is not
unhygienic, for omelets do not stick to a well-seasoned pan,
so that it is only necessary to rub surplus grease off it with
soft paper. The pan always remains very slightly greasy
and quite smooth, and the eggs do not stick to it.

The pan can be washed once when quite new and then
'seasoned'. To do this, heat some salt in it and rub it well
into the surface. Discard the salt, wipe the pan clean with a

soft cloth or paper and then heat a very small knob of lard in it. Heat until the lard smokes, pour it away, and polish the pan with soft paper.

When cooking an omelet, it is important to use oil or lard for frying or else to use clarified butter. If there is moisture in the fat, as there is in butter, or if there is any sediment when it is heated, as there is in dripping, butter, or margarine, the omelet may stick to the pan. Not only is it difficult to turn out a perfect omelet in these circumstances but it means the pan must be scoured to get it clean and then the next omelet will stick to it. Very little fat is needed or a greasy omelet will result. To clarify butter, heat it slowly in the pan until it stops bubbling. This means that the water has evaporated. Take a spoon and carefully lift out any sediment in the bottom of the pan so that only clear oil remains.

A small pan is required for omelets. A five-inch base will cook a two-egg omelet, a seven-inch will take a four-egg omelet and a nine-inch will take six eggs.

When the omelet mixture is ready to cook, put a little fat in the pan and heat until it smokes very, very faintly. Pour in the mixture. The heat of the pan will cause the edges to set at once. Take a fork and draw it across the base of the pan two or three times. This removes cooked egg from contact with the hot metal and prevents it becoming over-cooked. It also allows raw mixture to run down in its place and cook at once. An omelet should not be really firm throughout.

When most of the egg is coagulated and the top is still soft, tilt the pan and with the aid of a palette knife, fold the mixture double, bringing the brown underside of one half on top of the other half of the omelet. Turn out quickly on to a hot dish and serve at once. To turn out an omelet, either invert the pan or slide the omelet from the pan on to the serving dish.

A plain omelet consists of eggs, seasoning, and water only. Some cooks use milk but the result is slightly more rubbery and the omelet sticks more readily to the pan.

Herbs can be added to a plain omelet to give an Omelet Fines Herbes. Meat, bacon, cheese, fish, or vegetables can be added to omelets, but these are never stirred into the raw eggs as they would cause the omelet to stick to the pan. They are cooked (or reheated) in a separate pan and kept hot. When the omelet is ready for folding, the hot filling is put on to it.

PLAIN OMELET

INGREDIENTS

2 eggs	1 tablesp. water
½ oz. butter	Pepper and salt
Parsley	

METHOD

Break the eggs into a basin and add the seasoning and water. Beat until they are well-mixed but not foamy. Melt the butter in the pan and remove any sediment. Heat slowly until it stops bubbling and then raise the heat. Cook the omelet. Garnish with parsley.

OMELET FINES HERBES

Use the recipe for plain omelet and add to it a teaspoonful of finely chopped parsley, tarragon, and chervil. Chives can be used as well if their flavour is acceptable. Fresh herbs make the best omelet. Dried herbs are all too often used and the result is a travesty of the ideal.

CHEESE OMELET

Sprinkle grated cheese generously over the cooked mixture in the pan and fold at once.

OMELET WITH MEAT OR FISH

Left-over cold meat can be chopped or diced, heated in a little well-seasoned thick gravy or sauce, and placed in the cooked omelet when it is ready for folding. The meat mixture should not be too wet or there will be difficulty in turning the omelet on to the serving dish. Flaked cod or smoked fish treated similarly gives a pleasant filling.

MUSHROOM OMELET

Allow one to two ounces of mushrooms for every two eggs. Slice or dice them and put into a small pan with one teaspoonful of lemon juice and one tablespoonful of water to every four ounces of mushrooms. Cover with a lid and simmer for 3 minutes only. Add seasoning. Work one teaspoonful of flour into quarter of an ounce of butter and stir this into the mushroom mixture to bind it together. As soon as it boils it is ready to spread on the omelet.

ROES (COD'S)

Cod's roes can be purchased from the fishmonger already boiled, or they can be boiled at home. To boil:

Wash in salted water, place in a pan, and cover with water containing salt and lemon juice. Bring gently to the boil and simmer for about 15 minutes. Drain and cut into thick slices and serve with Hollandaise sauce. Garnish with parsley.

The most popular way of cooking cod's roe is frying. Take thick slices of boiled roe and dip in seasoned flour. Heat enough fat in a thick frying-pan to come half-way up the slices of roe. Lay these in the fat and cook gently until browned on the underside. Turn with a palette knife and brown on the second side. Drain on paper. Serve with a parsley garnish and tomato sauce.

SCOTCH EGGS: RECIPE 1

INGREDIENTS

2 hard boiled eggs	Flour
2 sausages (¼ lb.)	Egg and breadcrumbs

METHOD

When the eggs are cold, remove their shells and roll them in flour. Skin the sausages and flatten each one into a circle. Place an egg in the centre of each circle of sausage meat and work the sausage all over the egg smoothing the surface to remove cracks. Dip in beaten egg and then in breadcrumbs. Fry in deep fat until a good brown colour. Garnish with parsley and serve hot or allow to get cold and serve with salad.

SCOTCH EGGS: RECIPE 2

INGREDIENTS

2 hard-boiled eggs	¼ pt milk (short measure)
¾ oz. butter	4 oz. cooked, flaked smoked
1 oz. flour	haddock
Pepper and salt	Egg and breadcrumbs

METHOD

It is necessary that the haddock is flaked thoroughly or else the mixture will not adhere smoothly to the eggs and the surface will crack when they are fried. Melt the butter in a small pan and add the flour. Fry until a sandy texture but not coloured. Add most of the milk, all at once, and stir until boiling. Beat until smooth and season very well. Dilute with the remaining milk if necessary. This mixture should adhere to the spoon in a firm ball; if it spreads out in the pan it is too soft to fry without breaking; if it is very stiff it will be unpleasant to eat. Beat in the fish and leave to cool. Shell the eggs and roll in flour, divide the mixture into two and flatten into circles. Wrap one circle round each egg and smooth the surface. Dip in beaten egg and then in breadcrumbs. Fry in deep fat until a good brown colour. Serve hot with parsley garnish and lemon slices, or cold with salad.

Cooked minced meat can be used in place of fish. In this case, replace the milk in the above recipe by meat stock.

SPANISH EGGS

INGREDIENTS

3 hard-boiled eggs
8 oz. onions
8 oz. tomatoes
From a pinch to ⅛ teasp. each of powdered turmeric, cinnamon, ginger, and cloves

2 tablesps. oil
Bouquet garni
Pepper and salt and sugar
⅛ pt stock
2 tablesps. white wine
Parsley

METHOD

Skin the tomatoes and cut coarsely. Slice the onions. Heat the oil in a pan and cook the onions very slowly until clear. Add tomatoes and spices and cook a further 5 minutes. Add the stock, bouquet garni, seasoning, and wine and simmer until reduced by half. Cut the eggs in halves or slices and add them to this mixture. Heat through, remove the bouquet garni, and pour into a deep dish. Garnish with parsley.

Raw eggs can be broken individually into the tomato mixture and cooked in it instead of adding hard-boiled eggs.

SPANISH OMELET

INGREDIENTS

3 eggs

Salt and pepper

6 tablesps. vegetables (see   1 clove garlic
   below)   Oil or clarified butter

Mixed vegetables are used in this recipe and their choice is one of personal preference. Tomatoes and onions should be present and in addition to these carrot, turnips, peas, French beans, peppers, celery, and aubergine can be used. Any combination or all of them can appear in one omelet.

Cut all the vegetables into very tiny dice. Crush the garlic. Put a tablespoon of oil in a small, thick pan and add the garlic and prepared vegetables. Cover with a lid and cook slowly until tender. Remove the garlic and add seasoning. Keep this mixture hot.

Break the eggs into a bowl and beat them slightly, add salt and pepper. Put a little oil into a large omelet pan and heat until a very faint smoke appears. Add the vegetables and pour over them the eggs. Stir a little and then lower the heat and continue to cook the omelet undisturbed until it is firm enough to be turned with two broad knives or spatulas. Leave to set on the second side and then slide it on to a hot serving dish. This omelet is not folded.

Some chefs serve this dish with the cooked vegetables folded between the two thicknesses of a plain omelet instead of cooking them with the eggs.

STUFFED AUBERGINE

INGREDIENTS

2 small aubergines   4 tablesps. breadcrumbs
4 hard-boiled eggs   Tomato sauce
Pepper and salt   Parsley
1 oz. butter

METHOD

Wash the aubergines and steam until tender (20–30 min-

utes). Remove the stalk and cut in halves lengthwise. Scoop
out the pulp and chop it well. Chop the eggs and mix with
the pulp, salt, and pepper. Fill the half skins with this
mixture, sprinkle with breadcrumbs, and put small pats of
butter on the surface. Place on a greased baking tray and
heat in an oven at 450° until brown. This should take 5–10
minutes. Serve on an oval dish with parsley garnish. Pour
some of the tomato sauce round the vegetables and serve
the rest in the sauce-boat.

A little grated Parmesan cheese mixed with the breadcrumbs gives a pleasant crust to the filling. Cooked minced
meat, bacon, or ham, can be used in place of eggs.

STUFFED CABBAGE: RECIPE 1

INGREDIENTS

1 white-heart cabbage, medium size	1 turnip
	1 onion
¾ lb. sausage meat	Salt and pepper
½–¾ pt stock	Chopped parsley
Ketchup or Worcestershire sauce	¾ oz. flour
	Gravy browning
Bouquet garni	Dripping
1 carrot	

METHOD

Wash the cabbage and remove the outer leaves. Boil it whole
in salted water for 5 minutes and then drain it. Trim the
stalk so that the cabbage will stand upright in a dish. Carefully open the leaves and scoop out the inside, leaving the
outside whole. Chop the heart leaves and mix with the
sausage meat and some seasoning. A few drops of ketchup
or Worcestershire sauce can be added as well. Pack this into
the cabbage and tie the outer leaves round it. Place the
cabbage in a deep pan, pour stock round it, and add season-

ing, a bouquet garni, and the carrot, turnip, and onion cut into fairly small pieces. Cover with a lid. Bring to the boil and then lower the heat and simmer for 45 minutes. When the cabbage is tender, melt the dripping in a small pan, stir in the flour, and fry gently until fawn-coloured. Strain the stock from the cabbage and gradually work this into the fat and flour. Stir until boiling and then correct the seasoning. Add gravy browning. Put the cabbage in the serving dish, pour the sauce over it, and garnish with chopped parsley.

STUFFED CABBAGE: RECIPE 2

This recipe is a period piece. It is included more as an example of the lavishness with which our ancestors used butter and eggs rather than as a practical recipe for use today. It is doubtful whether today's tastes would be in sympathy with fish and cabbage in one dish.

INGREDIENTS

A white-heart cabbage, medium size	2 oz. butter
1–1½ lb. plaice fillets	½ oz. flour
4 hard-boiled eggs, chopped	An onion stuck with 6 cloves
2 tablesps. chopped parsley	
4 oz. melted butter	6 peppercorns and a small piece of blade mace tied in muslin
1 egg yolk	
1–2 tablesps. breadcrumbs	½ oz. morels and truffles
½ pt water	1 teasp. ketchup
Pepper and salt	A few pickled mushrooms

METHOD

Wash and trim the cabbage and boil whole in salted water for 5 minutes. Trim the stalk so that the cabbage will stand upright. Open the outer leaves and scoop out the heart. Chop the heart leaves. Skin the fish fillets. Mix together the

chopped cabbage, fish, four hard-boiled eggs, and the parsley.
Pound all these together in a mortar with four ounces melted
butter. When quite smooth add seasoning, one egg yolk,
and breadcrumbs. Pack into the cabbage and tie the outer
leaves around the stuffing. Put the cabbage into a deep pan
with half a pint of water, ketchup, the onion, peppercorns,
and mace. Add the truffles, morels, and mushrooms. Mix
two ounces of butter with half an ounce of flour and put
this in the pan. Add a little salt. Cover closely and simmer
for an hour. Remove the onion and spices, lay the cabbage
on a serving dish, and pour the sauce over it.

STUFFED MARROW

INGREDIENTS

1 *small marrow*	1 *small onion chopped*
8 oz. *chopped cooked meat*	2 oz. *dripping*
Thick gravy to moisten the meat	*Parsley*

METHOD

Wash the marrow and steam whole for 7 minutes. Peel it,
slit in halves lengthwise, and scoop out the seeds. Melt a
little dripping in a pan and fry the onions slowly until
clear. Add the onion to the cooked meat and moisten with
a little very thick gravy. Pack into both halves of the marrow
and place them together again. Tie together with broad tape
in at least two places.

Heat the dripping in a roasting tin and place the marrow
in it. Baste well. Cover with greased paper and roast in a
moderate oven (375°), with frequent basting, for 40 minutes
to 1 hour. When it is tender, lift on to a serving dish. Cut
the tapes and remove them. Garnish with parsley.

Very young marrows need not be peeled. If small marrows
are out of season, cut a large one into rings about three

inches long. Steam these and pack the stuffing into the centre of each. Care must be taken to lift the slices of marrow from the roasting tin with a fish slice or the stuffing will fall through them as they are being served.

STUFFED TOMATOES: RECIPE 1

INGREDIENTS

6 medium-sized tomatoes	Browned breadcrumbs
1 oz. finely chopped mushrooms	Pepper and salt
1 tablesp. breadcrumbs	1 oz. butter
½ teasp. finely chopped parsley	2 oz. finely chopped cooked chicken or ham

METHOD

Cut a slice off the bottom of each tomato, scoop out the pulp with a teaspoon, and invert the shells to drain. Melt the fat in a small frying-pan and add to it all the ingredients except the browned breadcrumbs. Stir over a low flame until well mixed and very hot. Fill the tomatoes with this mixture and sprinkle the top with browned breadcrumbs. Replace the slice which was cut off. Place on a greased baking tray and cover with greased paper. Bake in an oven at 375° until tomatoes are tender. Serve with a parsley garnish.

STUFFED TOMATOES: RECIPE 2

INGREDIENTS

4 large tomatoes	½ oz. grated cheese
4 eggs	Parsley

METHOD

Cut a slice off the bottom of each tomato, scoop out the pulp with a teaspoon, and invert the shells to drain. Season inside each tomato with pepper and salt. Break an egg into each. Sprinkle a little grated cheese over the top and replace the slice which was cut off. Place on a greased baking tray and bake in a moderate oven, 375°, until the tomato is tender. Serve with a parsley garnish.

VIENNESE CAULIFLOWER

INGREDIENTS

1 small cauliflower
4 oz. minced ham
2 egg yolks, or
   1 whole egg
1 gill of sour cream

1 oz. melted butter
1 tablesp. breadcrumbs
Pepper and salt
Parsley

METHOD

Break the cauliflower into sprigs and wash in cold water. Boil in salted water for 7 minutes and drain well. Grease a small, deep fireproof dish and put a layer of cauliflower in it. Sprinkle with ham. Repeat until the dish is full. Whip the egg yolks and season well. Stir in the sour cream and strain this custard over the cauliflower. Sprinkle the surface with breadcrumbs and then with melted butter. Bake in an oven (410°) for 20–25 minutes. Serve with a parsley garnish.

Sour cream is on sale in delicatessen stores and supermarkets but sour milk can be used instead.

CHAPTER 7

Sauces and Salad Dressings

BÉCHAMEL SAUCE

INGREDIENTS

1½ oz. butter
1½ oz. flour
1 pt milk
Bouquet garni, 1 clove, 6
  peppercorns, all tied in
  muslin

Salt
Small piece of carrot,
  turnip, and onion
1–2 tablesps. cream

METHOD

Put the vegetables and bouquet garni in a pan and add the milk. Heat until very warm and then leave in a warm place for 30 minutes. Strain. Melt the fat in a small pan and stir in the flour. Cook until it is a sandy texture but not coloured. Gradually add the flavoured milk, stirring the whole time. Stir until boiling and simmer for 3 minutes. Stir in the cream and serve.

BIGARADE SAUCE

INGREDIENTS

½ pt Espagnole sauce
1 shallot
Zest and juice of one orange
2 teasps. redcurrant jelly

¼ oz. butter
⅛ pt red wine
Cayenne pepper
1 teasp. lemon juice

METHOD

Pare the orange very thinly, taking only the zest, i.e. the deeply coloured portion, for the sauce. Chop the shallot and cook slowly in the butter until tender. Add the wine and redcurrant jelly. Simmer until the jelly dissolves. Add the Espagnole sauce, the orange juice, and half the orange rind cut into small pieces. Simmer for 10 minutes. While it is simmering, take the other half of the orange zest and cut into very small shreds. Drop these into boiling water, boil for 5 minutes, and then drain. Strain the sauce and return it to the pan with the blanched zest. Add cayenne pepper, salt, and lemon juice to taste.

BROWN SAUCE

INGREDIENTS

¾ oz. dripping	*Bouquet garni*
1 oz. flour	1 oz. *carrot*
¾ pt stock	1 oz. *onion*
Pepper and salt	1 oz. *turnip*

METHOD

Melt the dripping in a thick pan and fry the carrot, turnip, and onion until golden brown. Stir in the flour with a metal tablespoon and continue stirring constantly over a moderate heat until the flour is an even milk-chocolate colour. At *once* add all the stock or the flour will become too dark. Remove the pan from the stove to add the stock and then return it to the heat and stir until the sauce boils. Add the bouquet garni and seasoning. Put on a lid and simmer gently for 40 minutes. It must not reduce by evaporation. Remove any fat from the top, correct the seasoning, and strain.

If the flour is not browned sufficiently, the sauce will be pale and a little gravy browning may be necessary.

CHEESE SAUCE (MORNAY SAUCE)

INGREDIENTS

½ pt Béchamel sauce   1 teasp. made mustard
1½ oz. grated cheese   1–2 tablesps. cream

METHOD

Stir the grated cheese and mustard into the sauce just before
it is served and heat only long enough to melt the cheese.
Stir in the cream.

ESPAGNOLE SAUCE

This is a brown sauce with ham, tomatoes, mushrooms, and
sherry cooked in it.

INGREDIENTS

¾ oz. dripping   1 oz. turnip
1 oz. flour   1 tomato
¾ pt stock   2 mushrooms
Pepper and salt   2 oz. lean ham (or lean
Bouquet garni   bacon)
1 oz. carrot   1–2 tablesps. sherry
1 oz. onion

METHOD

Cut all the vegetables into fairly small pieces and cut up the
ham. Melt the fat and gently fry the carrot, turnip, onion,
and ham. Add the flour and stir over a moderate heat until
it is a milk-chocolate brown. Remove the pan from the heat
and *at once* add all the stock. Return to the stove and stir
until the sauce boils. Add the remaining ingredients and
simmer gently for 40 minutes to an hour, skimming off any
fat as it rises. Correct the seasoning and colour. Strain and serve.

If a good sherry is used, it is best to stir it in just before serving. An inferior or cooking sherry should be put in with the stock. If ham is not available a few bacon rinds can be used to give the desired flavour to this sauce, but the fat should be removed from them.

HOLLANDAISE SAUCE

INGREDIENTS

2 egg yolks

4 oz. butter

⅛ pt vinegar

⅛ pt water

3 peppercorns

Salt

METHOD

Put the vinegar, water, and peppercorns in a small pan and boil until only a teaspoonful of liquid remains. Strain this into a basin, allow it to cool, and then add the egg yolks. Keep a piece of butter the size of a hazel nut and put the remainder in a warm place before it is used so that it becomes really soft but not oiled. Place the basin of egg yolks over a pan of warm water and have a low heat under the pan. Whisk the eggs, the hazel nut of butter, and the vinegar until creamy and then add the remaining butter very gradually, a small amount at a time. Whisk constantly. As the sauce becomes thick, remove the basin from the hot water and continue adding the butter. Season with salt and, if necessary, a very little cayenne pepper. Serve lukewarm.

If the water beneath the sauce is too hot, the butter will become oil and separate from the eggs. Hollandaise sauce should never be allowed to reach a high temperature.

ITALIAN SAUCE

INGREDIENTS

½ pt Espagnole sauce

3 small shallots

1 sprig of thyme and

1 bay leaf tied in muslin

4 small mushrooms   ⅛ pt wine
1 tablesp. oil   ⅛ pt stock

METHOD

Skin the shallots and chop until extremely fine. Place into a
pan with the oil. Cook gently until clear but do not allow
them to brown. Pour off any surplus oil. Chop the mushrooms. Add the mushrooms, herbs, and stock to the pan
and boil until the volume is reduced to less than half. Add
the Espagnole sauce, cover with a lid, and simmer for 10
minutes. Remove the herbs, skim off any fat, correct the
seasoning, and serve.

MADEIRA SAUCE

INGREDIENTS

½ pt Espagnole sauce   2½ tablesps. Madeira wine

METHOD

Heat the Espagnole sauce over a flame until the volume is
reduced by at least a half and the consistency is thick.
Remove the pan from the heat and add the wine. Correct
the seasoning and strain through a nylon sieve. Return to
a clean pan and keep warm until required, but do not allow
to boil.

MAÎTRE D'HÔTEL BUTTER

INGREDIENTS

4 oz. butter   Juice of half a lemon
1 tablesp. chopped parsley   Salt and cayenne pepper

METHOD

Wring the chopped parsley in a dry cloth.

Beat the fat with a wooden spoon until it is pale and creamy. Add the lemon juice drop by drop, beating all the time. Season to taste and beat in the chopped parsley. Wrap in wet greaseproof paper and shape into a neat block or cylinder. Chill until firm and cut up neatly before serving.

MAYONNAISE

INGREDIENTS

1 egg yolk	½ teasp. sugar
¼ pt oil	¼ teasp. dry mustard
2 tablesps. vinegar	⅛ teasp. pepper
½ teasp. salt	

METHOD

Put the egg yolk and seasonings into a small basin. It is important that the basin has a small diameter, so that every time the whisk is moved it will pick up most of the egg and bring it into contact with the oil. Add the oil drop by drop, whisking all the time. When the mixture becomes very pale and stiff, whisk in half a tablespoonful of vinegar. The oil can then be added a teaspoonful at a time, still whisking. Each time the sauce becomes very thick, add a little vinegar. When all the oil is in, add more vinegar, if required, until the flavour is satisfactory. If the mayonnaise is too thick it can then be diluted with a little water.

If oil is added too quickly, the sauce will curdle. To correct this, take a fresh egg yolk and add the curdled sauce to it drop by drop until the mixture is thick and creamy, and then continue to work in any remaining oil. Malt vinegar can be used for mayonnaise, but part of it can be replaced by tarragon or chilli vinegar to give a superior flavour to the sauce. Do not add water to mayonnaise which is to be stored; dilute when it is required.

MUSTARD SAUCE: RECIPE 1

INGREDIENTS

½ pt Béchamel or Velouté
　　sauce
1 egg yolk

Cayenne pepper
1 tablesp. made mustard or
　　French mustard

METHOD

Make the white sauce, cool slightly, and pour it on to the beaten egg yolk. Stir in mustard and cayenne pepper, and return to the pan. Reheat gently and serve before it boils. If velouté sauce is used, a teaspoonful of vinegar can be added to mustard sauce. Malt vinegar can be used, but tarragon or chilli vinegar gives a better flavour. Vinegar cannot be added to a mustard sauce made with Béchamel sauce because it will make the milk curdle.

MUSTARD SAUCE: RECIPE 2

INGREDIENTS

½ pt brown sauce
1 teasp. chilli or tarragon
　　vinegar

1 dessertsp. French mustard
1 teasp. anchovy essence

METHOD

Mix all the ingredients and stir until boiling.

PARSLEY SAUCE

INGREDIENTS

½ pt Béchamel or Velouté
　　sauce

1 teasp. to 1 tablesp. finely
　　chopped parsley

METHOD

Wring the parsley dry in a clean cloth and stir into the boiling white sauce immediately before serving.

RÉMOULADE SAUCE

INGREDIENTS

¼ pt mayonnaise
1 teasp. chopped parsley,
  tarragon, and fennel, or
  chervil instead of fennel

1 teasp. made mustard
1 teasp. chopped capers and
  gherkins

METHOD

Chop the herbs finely, wring in a dry cloth, and mix with the mustard. Stir into the mayonnaise.

SOUR CREAM SALAD DRESSING: RECIPE 1

INGREDIENTS

¼ pt sour cream
1 teasp. made mustard
½ teasp. salt

1 dessertsp. sugar
Paprika or black pepper
2 tablesps. lemon juice

METHOD

Mix all these ingredients together and beat until stiff. Yoghourt can be used in the place of sour cream in this dressing.

SOUR CREAM SALAD DRESSING: RECIPE 2

INGREDIENTS

¼ pt sour cream
1 teasp. made mustard
½ teasp. salt

Paprika or black pepper
2 tablesps. vinegar
1 egg

METHOD

Beat the egg and add all the other ingredients. Place in a double saucepan or in a basin over a pan of hot water, and stir until the mixture thickens. Transfer at once to a cold vessel.

TARTARE·SAUCE

INGREDIENTS

¼ pt oil

1 hard-boiled egg yolk

1 raw egg yolk

1 teasp. chopped parsley, tarragon, and fennel, or chervil in place of fennel

1 teasp. chopped capers and gherkins

Vinegar to taste (about 2 tablesps.)

½ teasp. salt

¼ teasp. mustard

⅛ teasp. pepper

½ teasp. sugar

METHOD

Sieve the hard-boiled egg yolk into a small basin. Add salt, pepper, mustard, and sugar. Gradually work in the raw egg yolk and then continue as for mayonnaise. Wring the chopped herbs in a dry cloth and stir these into the sauce together with the capers and gherkins.

TOMATO SAUCE

INGREDIENTS

½ lb. tomatoes

¼ pt stock

Small piece of onion

Small piece of carrot

½ teasp. sugar

½ oz. butter

Pepper and salt

Bouquet garni

¼ oz. cornflour (good weight)

METHOD

Wash and slice the tomatoes. Peel and slice the carrot and onion. Put the vegetables and butter into a thick pan and stir until the butter is melted. Add seasoning. Cover with a lid and cook over a slow heat for 10 minutes. Add the stock and bouquet garni and bring quickly to the boil. Lower the heat and simmer for 30 minutes with a lid on the pan. Rub through a nylon sieve. Blend the cornflour with a little cold stock and gradually add to the sauce, stirring well. Return to the pan and stir until boiling. Correct consistency and seasoning.

VELOUTÉ SAUCE

INGREDIENTS

½ oz. butter
½ oz. flour
½ pt white stock

Salt and pepper
Few drops of lemon juice

METHOD

The stock for this sauce should be made with white meat or its bones, e.g. chicken, veal. If the velouté sauce is to be used with fish, the stock should be made with fish trimmings.

Melt the fat and add the flour. Stir over the heat until of a sandy texture but not coloured. Gradually add the stock and then stir until boiling. Season and add the lemon juice. Simmer for 3 minutes.

Chefs do not use velouté sauce alone, but as the basis for many other sauces, all of which call for the addition of other ingredients. In the home, velouté sauce is often served as such, though it will be much improved if three or four tablespoons of cream are stirred in after it is cooked.

VINAIGRETTE (FRENCH DRESSING)

INGREDIENTS

3 tablesps. oil
1 tablesp. vinegar
1 clove garlic
1 teasp. salt

½ teasp. paprika or a little
    black pepper
1 teasp. sugar
1 teasp. made mustard

METHOD

Mix the vinegar, mustard, and seasonings. Pour slowly on to the oil, whisking vigorously all the time. Continue to whisk until the sauce is thick and cloudy. Correct the seasoning and use at once.

A clove of garlic should be crushed before use. If a strong garlic flavour is required, leave the clove to steep in vinegar for 30 minutes before the sauce is whisked. If a milder flavour is required, the garlic should be rubbed round the basin and then discarded. The best flavour is given by a mixture of wine vinegar and tarragon vinegar. Half the vinegar can be replaced by lemon juice.

Vinaigrette to pour over orange salad can be made with brandy instead of vinegar.

A very easy way to make vinaigrette is to put all the ingredients together into a small bottle with a screw top and to shake vigorously until the mixture is thick and cloudy.

VINAIGRETTE WITH CREAM

INGREDIENTS

Equal quantities of vinaigrette and cream.

METHOD

Beat the cream until slightly stiff and beat in the vinaigrette.

CHAPTER 8

Salads

MOST people think of eating for slimming in terms of
salads. But just because our slimming principles stress foods
like meat and fats and eggs and cheese, we do not have to
avoid salads altogether. They make some of the most interesting and attractive dishes, and are quite rightly increasingly
popular with all sorts of people, overweight or otherwise.
There is, however, a tendency to be too conservative in
choice and blends of vegetables. Although there are many
recipes for salads composed of raw or cooked foods, do try
your own experiments with unusual combinations of tex-
tures and flavours. There are many who enjoy originality
not only in preparing but also in serving foods. For example,
they make and decorate salads with edible flowers – nastur-
tiums not only look attractive but they also have a distinctive flavour.

Salads of raw vegetables should be crisp and clean, should
not appear to suffer from overhandling, and should be dry.
Salad baskets are available for drying washed lettuce or
watercress, but swinging them in a clean tea towel is an
adequate method. There should never be surplus water in
the serving bowl. Salads should be prepared only a very
short time before they are eaten so that their appearance and
crispness are at their best. Chilling a salad briefly in the
refrigerator gives it a crisp texture and makes it refreshing
in hot weather. The dish should be covered, or moisture
will evaporate from the leaves and they will become limp.

Fruits blend well with vegetables and avocado or dessert
pears, apples, pineapples, and bananas are often used in

salads. The cut surfaces of pears, apples, and bananas darken quickly on exposure to air. If they are brushed with lemon juice or soaked briefly in water and lemon juice, they remain white. Tinned fruits preserved in water rather than syrup may also be used, or the fruit drained well from the syrup.

*

AVOCADO PEAR

The halved pear is often served as the first course of a lunch or dinner. It is cut in halves lengthwise and the stone is removed. The cut surfaces are brushed with lemon juice. The hollow which held the stone can be filled with one of several things:

1. *Lemon juice.*
2. *Vinaigrette.*
3. *Mayonnaise.*
4. *Mayonnaise with chopped prawns or other fish.*
5. *Cream cheese with Worcestershire sauce.*
6. *Any alternative which appeals to the cook.*

The flesh can be scooped out of the peel and mashed (or preferably sieved) with a little lemon juice and seasoning and then chopped chives or cream cheese or mayonnaise mixed with it. Imagination will lengthen this list, remembering that any added flavour should not be strong enough to mask the delicate flavour of the pear itself. The filling should be piled or piped into the empty peel, and chopped parsley and paprika pepper placed on the surface to garnish.

Avocado pears can be used in mixed salads. Dice the flesh, mix with equal amounts of diced cucumber and tomato, and moisten with vinaigrette. Chill before serving. Seasoning is necessary, and chopped fresh herbs sprinkled on top improve both appearance and flavour.

There are many other fruits and vegetables which marry well with avocado: celery, melon, apple, orange, banana, peeled grapes, or diced red or green peppers. The mixture used in salads can be varied on different occasions. Broken walnuts for example can be added to the mixture. When prepared, the salad can be served on a bed of lettuce leaves or spooned into orange peel cases. Red apples also provide an attractive case to hold this salad. Cut a slice from the top of the apple and scoop out the flesh with a spoon until only a thin layer remains to support the peel. Diced apple taken from prepared cases can be added to the salad.

Yet another way of serving avocado pear is to halve it, remove the stone and peel thinly. Place each half pear on a lettuce leaf and coat with vinaigrette. Serve with the hollow side uppermost and with small sprigs of watercress put in the centre. Chopped watercress and chives can be added to the dressing as can finely chopped Danish blue cheese.

BANANA AND CHEESE SALAD

Peel a banana and cut into two lengthwise and across. Brush the four pieces with lemon juice. Lay two pieces on each of two plates. Pile cream cheese or sour milk cheese on the centre and place heart leaves of lettuce between the pieces of banana. Place pieces of tomato, sprigs of watercress, and diced, cooked beetroot in the lettuce leaves. Sprinkle the cheese with chopped mixed herbs or with chopped parsley.

CELERY AND APPLE SALAD

Dice equal amounts of celery and sharp apple, e.g. russet. Soak in water and lemon juice for 5 minutes and drain well. Add one-third this amount of broken walnuts and serve in a neat pile with lettuce, watercress, and tomato round the edge.

CHICORY SALAD

Strip any blemished leaves from heads of chicory, wash and
drain. Break into separate leaves, or cut each head into half-
inch slices. Toss in a vinaigrette dressing and transfer to
a serving dish and serve at once, sprinkled with chopped
parsley or chopped fresh herbs. Tarragon, chervil, and parsley blend well. Chives can be used alone or with mixed
herbs. Fennel can be used, especially when the salad accompanies fish.

CUCUMBER AND SHRIMP SALAD

Cut a cucumber in halves lengthwise and scoop out the flesh.
Dice the flesh and mix with peas and shrimps or with
broken pieces of lobster or crawfish. Moisten with vinaigrette or mayonnaise and replace in the cucumber skins.
Sprinkle with chopped fresh herbs.

Individual servings of this salad can be made by cutting
the cucumber into two-inch lengths and scooping most of
the flesh out but leaving a little at one end of each portion.
Pieces then stand on a cut surface and form small cups to
hold the filling. A 'handle' made from cucumber skin or
parsley or watercress stalk can be inserted in the filling to
give the appearance of baskets. White meat can be used in
place of fish in this salad.

CREAM CHEESE AND PINEAPPLE

For this dish, cream cheese, curd cheese, or Demisel cheese
can be used. Shape the cheese into blocks or spheres or pipe
it through a vegetable star pipe on to the centre of a circle
of pineapple and place this on a serving plate. About two
ounces of cheese per portion is the usual serving. Sprinkle

chopped fresh herbs on top of the cheese. Decorate with heart leaves of lettuce around the edge of the plate. Other salad vegetables can be included.

Pears can replace pineapple in this salad.

COLESLAW

This popular American salad does not receive the attention it deserves in Great Britain. A white Dutch cabbage with its typical sweet flavour is the chief ingredient.

Cut the cabbage in quarters and remove the stalk. Shred across each section of cabbage so that paper-thin strips are produced. Put these into cold water, preferably with ice in it, and keep in a cold place for several hours. Drain and dry very thoroughly, using a clean tea towel or a salad basket to remove all the water. Mix the shredded cabbage with a large amount of cooked sour-cream dressing or with cooked salad dressing (see below) and pile on to a serving dish.

COLESLAW DRESSING (RECIPE 1)

INGREDIENTS

1 teasp. salt	1 teasp. made mustard
2 teasp. sugar	Pinch of cayenne pepper
2 tablesps. flour	1 or 2 egg yolks
1 oz. butter	⅓ pt milk
4 tablesps. vinegar	

METHOD

Scald and cool the milk. Beat the egg slightly and add the milk. Put the dry ingredients and mustard in the top of a double pan and gradually blend in the milk and egg. Add the vinegar and butter. Stir over hot water until the mixture becomes thick. Strain and use when cold.

COLESLAW DRESSING (RECIPE 2)

INGREDIENTS

1 teasp. salt
1 teasp. made mustard
1½ tablesps. flour
2 tablesps. salad oil
4 tablesps. vinegar

2 teasps. sugar
Pinch of cayenne pepper
1 egg
¼ pt evaporated milk
3 tablesps. hot water

METHOD

Beat the egg and milk. Put the dry ingredients and mustard into the top of a double pan and gradually add the egg and milk. Add the remaining ingredients and stir over the hot water until thick. Strain and use when cold.

If these dressings are too thick they can be blended with a little cream, milk, or evaporated milk. They will store for several days in the refrigerator and should be thinned just before use.

COLESLAW PIQUANTE

This recipe requires three cups of shredded cabbage and one tablespoonful each of chopped green pepper, chopped red pepper, and pickle. Prepare and serve as for coleslaw.

To vary coleslaw, chopped celery, apple, nuts, and the diced flesh of oranges can be added on separate occasions.

FRENCH SALADS

French salad is made with one vegetable only which is dressed with vinaigrette. Prepare the vegetable according to its kind, e.g. wash and slice chicory or break into separate leaves; wash a head of endive, Batavian endive, or lettuce and separate into leaves; wash and pick sprigs of watercress.

Thoroughly dry the vegetable. Prepare vinaigrette and pour it over the vegetable in a large bowl. Toss quickly and lightly with two spoons so that the leaves are not bruised. Transfer at once to a serving dish and serve immediately. Chopped fresh herbs can be sprinkled on top.

Dandelion leaves can be used for French salad. They have a slightly bitter flavour and should be blanched before they are picked. To blanch dandelion leaves, invert a flower-pot over the leaves while they are growing and leave it there until they become pale.

Tomato cannot be tossed without spoiling its appearance. Skin and slice tomatoes and lay the overlapping slices on a serving dish. Pour vinaigrette over the slices and sprinkle with chopped parsley, chopped chives, or chopped basil.

A connoisseur will prefer to mix the dressing at the table and pour it over the vegetable as it is to be eaten.

GLOBE ARTICHOKE SALAD

Cook the artichokes in boiling salted water until they are tender enough for the leaves to be removed. Drain upside down on a cloth placed in a colander and leave them till cold. Remove the leaves and choke (see page 196), and reserve the bottom only. Dress with mayonnaise and serve in a salad bowl.

HOLLANDAISE SALAD

Cut into small dice the flesh of equal quantities of dessert apple, of boiled beetroot, and of boiled potato, and the flesh of salt or smoked herring such as red herring or bloater. Place into a bowl. Add a little chopped onion and French mustard, season well, and bind with mayonnaise. Place on a flat serving dish and smooth the top lightly. Make a trellis on top with thin strips of herring. Cut a hard-boiled egg into eight sections and place these within the trellis. Cut a gherkin into thin slices and lay these round the edges of the salad.

LETTUCE AND LEEK SALAD

Wash, dry, and shred a lettuce and the white part of a raw leek. Cut two ounces of lean gammon into tiny dice and fry in a little bacon fat. Add to this two tablespoons of vinegar and a little salt and pepper. Mix this with the prepared vegetables and serve in a bowl.

MACEDOINE SALAD

This is made with vegetables only. It is often called Russian salad, but the latter has many additional ingredients (see recipe). To prepare Macedoine salad, cook young spring carrots, turnips, green peas, and French beans separately in boiling salted water until tender. Dice the carrot, turnip and beans approximately the size of the peas. When cold, mix with mayonnaise and pile into a serving dish. Sprinkle with chopped mint or chopped parsley.

This salad can be made with old or with frozen vegetables in winter, but the delicate flavour of spring vegetables is obviously lacking.

MIXED SALAD

INGREDIENTS

1 lettuce	½ bunch radishes
1 bunch watercress	¼ punnet mustard and cress
½ cucumber	2–3 spring onions
3 tomatoes	1 hard-boiled egg

METHOD

Trim, wash, and dry the lettuce, mustard and cress, and

watercress. Skin the tomatoes and slice or cut into sections. Peel and slice the cucumber. Trim the radishes: cut nearly to the base with two or four cuts and soak in cold water until they are open. Trim the onions. Tear the outer lettuce leaves into pieces and place in a serving bowl. Arrange all the other vegetables decoratively on top, together with slices of egg. The salad can be arranged on a flat dish. Chop the onion if it is universally popular, but serve whole if there is any doubt. Pass dressing separately.

ONION AND TOMATO SALAD

Skin one pound of tomatoes, cut in halves, and remove the seeds. Dice the flesh and put into a bowl. Take the white parts of a bunch of spring onions or one large root onion and chop coarsely. Pour boiling water over the onion and leave for 10 minutes. Drain and allow to get quite cold. Add the onion to the tomato and mix them together with sufficient vinaigrette to moisten. Serve with chopped parsley.

ORANGE SALAD: Recipe 1

INGREDIENTS

2 oranges	Pepper and salt
1 slice pineapple	Lettuce leaves
2 small tomatoes	3 tablesps. cream
1 teasp. sugar	1 tablesp. vinegar

METHOD

Cut a slice from the top of each orange and scoop out the pulp with a spoon. Dice the flesh and put it in a bowl. Dice the pineapple and add to the orange. Skin the tomato, remove the seeds, and dice the flesh. Add this to the pineapple and orange. Sprinkle with sugar and leave for 30 minutes. In another basin, whisk together the cream and vinegar and season well with pepper and salt. Add this to the fruits and put them back into the orange cases. Serve on lettuce leaves.

There are many variations on this theme. Tomato and orange alone make a pleasant salad. Diced celery and apple can be used instead of pineapple and tomato. Very thin small shreds of lettuce leaves or coarsely chopped nuts can be mixed with the diced fruit and vegetables.

Yoghourt seasoned with pepper and salt can replace the cream dressing.

ORANGE SALAD: Recipe 2

INGREDIENTS

2 oranges
Vinaigrette

1 teasp. caster sugar
Watercress or celery curls

METHOD

Cut a strip about one inch wide from the zest of one orange, and cut this strip into three lengthwise and then cut across into tiny slivers. Drop these into boiling water and boil for 5 minutes. Drain and drop into cold water until cold and then drain again. Remove the rind and all the pith from both oranges. Cut them across into thin slices or, better still, cut the flesh from each segment with a sharp knife, leaving behind all the membrane and the central pith. Arrange the orange sections on a dish and sprinkle with caster sugar. Pour vinaigrette over them and sprinkle the prepared zest on top. Place small sprigs of watercress or curls of celery (see page 194) all round the edge of the dish.

This salad is excellent with duck. It is improved if the vinaigrette is made with brandy instead of part or all of the vinegar.

PEAR AND LETTUCE SALAD

Take halves of tinned or stewed pear and drain well and dry
with a cloth. Lay each half with the cut side downwards on
a serving plate. Mask with mayonnaise, sprinkle with a
tablespoonful of finely chopped red peppers, and arrange
lettuce leaves around the pear.

PRAWN SALAD

INGREDIENTS

¼ pt mayonnaise
1 pt aspic jelly
1 tablesp. chopped red or
    green pepper
1 teasp. chopped gherkins
2 oz. prawns

Diced cooked French beans,
    carrots, and mushrooms
Cooked peas
6 anchovy fillets
Lettuce, watercress, tomato,
    and radishes

METHOD

Fill a ring-shaped mould with cooked vegetables and diced
anchovy fillets and cover with cold aspic jelly. Leave to set.
Dip the mould quickly into hot water and turn on to a
serving dish. Surround with salad vegetables. Mix the
mayonnaise, chopped peppers, and gherkins and pile in the
centre of the ring. Arrange the prawns on top of the mayonnaise and on the aspic ring.

This is much improved if more prawns are used, including
some in the jelly.

RUSSIAN SALAD

Russian salad contains the ingredients of Macedoine salad
and, in addition, diced cooked chicken, ham or tongue, and
shrimps or diced lobster or crayfish, and also anchovy fillets.

Chopped capers, gherkins, and olives are frequently added. Chopped fresh herbs, usually tarragon, chervil, parsley, and probably chives, are also required.

Dice the meat and fish to match the diced vegetables in size. Chop the herbs, capers, gherkins, and olives finely. Mix all the ingredients in a bowl with sufficient mayonnaise to bind them together. Pile into a serving dish. A brightly coloured and bold garnish is needed to be effective – this is usually made from neatly cut pieces of beetroot, hard-boiled egg, pickled walnut, tongue, anchovy fillets, and shrimps.

Traditionally, a depression is made in the centre of the pile and caviar is put into it. Today, this addition to a Russian salad is very rarely met.

SPINACH AND LETTUCE SALAD

Wash a lettuce. Take an equal quantity of spinach leaves and wash these. Dry both vegetables thoroughly and slice with a sharp knife. Mix together with a little vinaigrette well-flavoured with garlic. Serve in a bowl with sieved hard-boiled egg on top.

SWEET CORN SALAD

Take freshly cooked or canned sweet corn and separate the corn from the cob with a fork. Season with pepper and salt and add a little lemon juice. To every cupful of corn take two ounces of button mushrooms. Trim the mushrooms and put into a small pan with pepper, salt, and a teaspoonful of water and a teaspoonful of lemon juice. Simmer for 3 minutes only. Cool and drain. Mix these with the corn and bind all together with fresh cream, sour cream, or yoghourt. Pile on a dish and sprinkle with chopped spring onion. When spring onions are not in season, a clove of garlic can be added to the mushrooms but removed before they are drained.

STUFFED TOMATOES

Tomatoes can be stuffed with many fillings and served on a bed of green salad plants, or used for picnic meals. Several fillings are suggested but there are others which can be used.

Prepare the tomato, cut a slice from the base (it will stand more firmly on the stalk end when served), and scoop out all the flesh with a teaspoon. Invert on a plate and leave to drain. The skin can be removed or retained. Pack with filling and chill before serving.

FILLINGS

1. Scrambled egg with some of the tomato pulp added or with chopped mushrooms or with chopped spring onion.
2. Chopped hard-boiled egg with mayonnaise.
3. Sour milk or cream cheese with chopped walnuts, capers, gherkins, and olives, or with Worcestershire sauce.
4. Grated cheese, chopped peppers, and mayonnaise with added mustard.
5. Shrimps in Béchamel sauce or mayonnaise.
6. Diced cold chicken or other meat in Béchamel sauce. If beef is used, a thick brown sauce or gravy is better than Béchamel sauce and a little horseradish sauce should be added.
7. Macedoine of vegetables in mayonnaise.
8. Diced, cooked mushrooms, and cauliflower sprigs with chopped fresh herbs and tomato sauce.
9. Canned tuna, salmon, or kippered herring mashed and mixed with sour cream and a little made mustard.
10. Corn and mushroom salad.

TOMATO AND PEPPER SALAD

For this two large tomatoes and one medium-sized green

pepper are required. Cut a slice off the top of each tomato and remove the seeds and flesh. Cut the stalk from the pepper and remove all the seeds, but keep the pepper in one piece. Mix together half a pound of sour milk or cream cheese, a tablespoon of chopped fresh herbs, a tablespoonful of chopped pickled walnut, and a few drops of mushroom ketchup or Worcestershire sauce. Chopped capers, gherkins, and olives can also be added. Pack this mixture into the tomatoes and pepper, pressing down well. Chill in a refrigerator for at least an hour. Take a sharp knife and cut the tomatoes and peppers into thin slices. Lay alternate slices of stuffed tomato and stuffed pepper on a serving dish, overlapping slightly. Sprinkle with chopped spring onion. Arrange heart leaves of lettuce, watercress sprigs, and mustard and cress round the dish.

TOMATO JELLY SALAD

INGREDIENTS

½ oz. gelatine	2 tablesps. malt vinegar
¾ pt tomato juice	1 tablesp. échalot vinegar
4 tablesps. water	¼ lb. shredded white
Piece of bay leaf	cabbage, or endive
½ teasp. salt	Lettuce leaves
1 dessertsp. sugar	Mayonnaise
1 tablesp. lemon juice	Chopped cucumber

If échalot vinegar is not used, a teaspoonful of chopped onion can be added to the tomato juice.

METHOD

Soak the gelatine in cold water in a saucepan for 5 minutes. Add the tomato juice, bay leaf, salt, and sugar and stir over a slow flame until the gelatine crystals have all dissolved. Cool and stir in the lemon juice and vinegar. Strain and allow to get completely cold. Add the shredded cabbage and endive (or any other vegetable or mixture of vegetables or diced meat and fish which may be considered suitable) and pour into a ring mould. Leave until set. Dip quickly into hot water and turn out on to a serving dish. Surround with lettuce leaves and fill the centre of the ring with mayonnaise mixed with finely chopped cucumber.

TURBOT SALAD

INGREDIENTS

8 oz. cooked turbot	Lettuce
Mayonnaise	Pepper and salt
2 oz. cooked potato or boiled rice	Cress
	Radishes

METHOD

The turbot should weigh eight ounces after all the skin and bone have been removed. Flake the fish or cut it into small dice. Shred a little lettuce into very tiny shreds. Dice the potatoes. Mix these three foods with sufficient mayonnaise to moisten and add pepper and salt. Pile in a serving dish and garnish with lettuce leaves, cress, and radishes.

An alternative way to serve this salad is to pack the fish mixture into a basin and place a saucer on top with a weight to hold it down. Chill for 2 hours and then invert the bowl of fish on to a serving dish and garnish.

Peas can be used instead of potatoes and any cooked white fish can be used in place of turbot.

WINTER SALAD

When fresh salad vegetables are scarce, a pleasant winter dish can be made from cooked diced carrot, turnip, potato, celeriac, brussels sprouts, cauliflower sprigs, cooked peas, and any other available vegetables. In addition, chopped nuts, shredded celery, diced raw apple (soaked in lemon juice and water to prevent discoloration), diced cooked beetroot, raw tomato, and watercress sprigs are used.

There are two ways in which this salad can be served:

1. Place each vegetable in a neat line across a dish. Alternate a pale one with a brightly coloured one and garnish the whole with watercress and tomato segments. Serve a dressing separately.

2. Mix the cooked vegetables (excluding beetroot) with a little mayonnaise or prepared dressing (see below) and pile on to a dish. Use tomato, watercress, beetroot, and curled celery as a garnish. Beetroot 'bleeds' and gives an uneven pink shade to the dressing if it is mixed in with the other vegetables.

Celery curls are prepared by cutting celery stalks into two-inch lengths and shaving paper-thin strips off. The strips are soaked in cold water till they curl up, and drained very well before use. Tomatoes may be omitted from this salad if it is made at a season when they are very expensive.

DRESSING FOR WINTER SALAD

INGREDIENTS

2 hard-boiled egg yolks   ½ teasp. sugar to taste
¼ teasp. salt   2–3 tablesps. vinegar
⅛ teasp. pepper   ¼ pt cream
¼ teasp. mustard

METHOD

Pound the yolks and seasonings together. Gradually work in the vinegar stirring all the time. Stir in the cream.

Coleslaw dressing is also suitable for serving with winter salad.

CHAPTER 9

Vegetables

IT is assumed that recipes for boiled cabbage, brussels sprouts, turnips, and other everyday vegetables are not necessary. A small selection of alternative ways of cooking and serving popular vegetables is given below.

It is well to remember, however, that the best flavour is obtained when green vegetables are cooked in about half an inch of boiling salted water. This also retains most of the valuable vitamins and mineral elements. If the pan is covered with a lid, steam is entrapped and cooks any leaves which are not submerged. The vegetable should be drained while there is still a little 'bite' in it. If it cooks for longer the nutritive value, colour, and flavour deteriorate. It should be drained immediately it is done, for if it stands in hot cooking water it will become water-logged. Winter and Savoy cabbage are usually reheated and glazed after they have been drained. The pan in which they were cooked is already hot, and a knob of margarine should be melted in it. The vegetable is then returned to this pan, seasoning is added, and it is stirred lightly until the leaves are coated with melted fat and are piping hot.

Cabbage, spring greens, kale, and other large leaves are more quickly and evenly cooked if they are shredded immediately before cooking. A really sharp knife is necessary. It is not advisable to shred and then soak in water, since soluble nutrients will dissolve into the soaking water and be lost. Cut the cabbage into quarters, or break off individual leaves, and wash until completely clean. Bring the cooking water to the boil and then drain and shred the vegetables and cook at once.

There are recipes for vegetables in other sections of this book, e.g. in 'Supper Dishes'.

*

ARTICHOKES

Globe artichokes are generally boiled. Cut the stalks close to the leaves, remove the outside leaves and trim about an inch off the tips of the remaining ones with scissors. Wash well under a cold tap and leave to soak in water with lemon juice in it. Cook in boiling salted water until tender, 25–40 minutes according to size. Artichokes are done when the leaves can easily be pulled off. Drain upside down on a cloth and serve hot on a napkin with melted butter or Hollandaise sauce passed separately.

Globe artichokes are excellent if served cold; a vinaigrette is the most suitable sauce to accompany them. It is also possible to stuff globe artichokes. Drain the cooked artichokes and then pull out the heart and discard the hairy choke, which is not edible. Fill the cavity in the centre with a savoury mixture of chopped cooked chicken, ham or other meat, reheated in a well-flavoured sauce. Replace the heart on top of the stuffing. Alternatively, remove the choke from raw artichokes and replace with stuffing and then cook the vegetables in a covered casserole in the oven, or in a deep pan on top of the stove. The pan should be brushed with oil before the artichokes are put in and about a glassful of white wine added for every four to six vegetables. They should simmer gently for an hour. The stuffing will be more pleasant to eat if it is rather dry before cooking, since it absorbs liquid as it cooks. Seasoning, herbs, and chopped meat, ham, or fish mixed with breadcrumbs give a pleasant stuffing.

Very small globe artichokes (one and a half to two inches long) can be fried whole in a deep layer of hot oil. When tender they are drained on kitchen paper, seasoned with pepper and salt, and the leaves are turned back slightly so that each artichoke looks like a flower. With such tiny vegetables there is no need to discard the choke.

Artichoke bottoms are greatly prized in France. To prepare them, remove the leaves, heart, and choke so that only the base is left. Trim this with a sharp knife so that it resembles a mushroom, brush with lemon juice, and then put it into a pan containing a shallow layer of boiling, salted water with four to six tablespoons of lemon juice to every pint of water. Press a piece of buttered paper on the artichokes and put a lid on the pan. Simmer until tender – probably about 25 minutes. Drain and coat with sauce before serving. Cheese sauce, brown sauce, or white sauce can be used. They can also be served cold with vinaigrette or mayonnaise. Artichoke bottoms are served plain or with meat or scrambled eggs or asparagus tips or minced mushrooms or a purée of vegetables spread on each one.

JERUSALEM ARTICHOKES

These vegetables darken after peeling if they are exposed to the air. They can be kept white if they are peeled under the surface of water to which lemon juice has been added. They should be soaked in clean, acidulated water until they are cooked, and they should be cooked in boiling water to which salt and lemon juice have been added. It is said that artichokes are cooked when they rise to the top of the pan, but large ones are not always tender when they rise. It is safer to pierce them with a skewer to be sure they are soft before draining them. The time taken to cook them depends on their size, but is generally from 10–20 minutes. They are dropped into fast-boiling, salted, acidulated water and allowed to boil quickly until done. They are then drained and served, generally with a Béchamel sauce poured over them.

ARTICHOKES CONSERVATIVE

Scrub and peel Jerusalem artichokes and cut into fairly thick slices. Soak in water and lemon juice for 30 minutes. Allow one to one and a half ounces of butter for every pound of artichokes and put this fat into a thick pan or casserole. Lift the artichokes out of water and place them in the pan. Season with pepper and salt. Place a sheet of buttered paper over the vegetables and put a lid on the pan. Cook over a very slow flame until tender (30–40 minutes) or in a slow oven (325°). If the heat is too fierce, the artichokes will become dry and burn, but if they are cooked gently they do not brown at all. Serve with chopped parsley sprinkled on top.

AUBERGINES

Aubergines are frequently sliced with the skin on and dipped in seasoned flour and then fried for about 10–15 minutes in shallow fat. They can also be fried in deep fat if they are first coated with egg and dusted with breadcrumbs. The slices can be grilled instead of fried but in this case it is advisable to brush with oil before putting them under a grill. A garnish of chopped parsley or fresh mixed herbs is usual. The flavour of an aubergine is thought to be improved if salt is sprinkled over the cut surfaces and left for an hour before cooking. This withdraws much of the moisture from the vegetable, but the salt should be washed off before cooking.

Diced aubergine and chopped garlic fried together in oil have a good flavour.

Aubergine is frequently served stuffed. Here again there are alternative means of preparation. Either the aubergine can be split in two and fried in hot fat for 3 minutes before scooping out the pulp, or the pulp can be removed while the vegetable is raw. In either case the pulp is chopped up and mixed with hard-boiled eggs and anchovy sauce or with cooked mushrooms or with any finely divided cooked meat in a thickened sauce or even with chopped ham and cooked onion mixed with breadcrumbs. The stuffing is seasoned well and piled in a half shell. The surface is sprinkled with breadcrumbs and small pieces of butter are placed on top. The stuffed aubergine is placed in a greased baking dish, covered with greased paper, and heated in an oven at 420° for 10–20 minutes. A well-flavoured tomato sauce should accompany it. Aubergines and cheese mix happily. In Italy an aubergine pie is prepared as follows:

INGREDIENTS

1 lb. aubergines	Oil
3–4 oz. Bel Paese cheese	Pepper and salt
½ oz. grated Parmesan	Flour
cheese	Browned breadcrumbs
¼ pt tomato sauce	

METHOD

Peel the aubergines and cut into thin slices. Sprinkle with salt and stand for an hour. Drain well, or wash and dry. Dip the slices of aubergine in flour seasoned with pepper and salt and fry them in oil until tender. Grease a fireproof dish, put a layer of aubergine slices on the bottom, cover with sliced Bel Paese cheese and continue until the vegetable is all used. Pour freshly made tomato sauce on top and sprinkle with grated Parmesan cheese and about a teaspoonful of browned breadcrumbs. Bake in a moderately hot oven (375°) for 30 minutes.

BRAISED CELERY

INGREDIENTS

1 large head of celery	Bacon rinds or 1 oz. lean
4 oz. carrot	ham

4 oz. onion	½ oz. dripping
1–2 level teasps. arrowroot or cornflour blended with a little cold stock	Salt, pepper, and a bouquet garni
2 oz. turnip	Gravy browning
	Parsley

METHOD

Scrub the celery and cut into fairly short lengths. Tie together into bundles. Peel the remaining vegetables and cut into fairly large pieces. Melt the dripping in a thick pan and fry the ham, carrot, turnip, onion, and any trimmings of celery until brown. Pour off excess fat and add the stock, seasoning, and bouquet garni. Place the celery on top. Cover with greased paper and a tightly fitting lid and cook gently on a slow heat or in an oven at 325° until tender. This will take from 1–2 hours. Lift the celery out on to a hot vegetable dish and remove the string. Add the blended cornflour to the stock in the pan and stir until boiling. Add gravy browning if necessary, correct seasoning, and strain over the celery. Garnish with parsley.

CABBAGE ÉTUVÉ

INGREDIENTS

1 cabbage	Pepper and salt
½ oz. sugar	1 onion
2–3 oz. butter	1 clove

METHOD

Cut the cabbage into quarters and wash. Remove the centre stalk and shred the leaves into a fine Julienne. Drop into boiling salted water for 3 minutes, drain in a colander, and run the cold tap through the shreds. Place them in a casserole with pepper, salt, and sugar. Peel the onion and stick the clove in it and place this in the casserole. Divide the fat into small pieces and put over the surface of the cabbage. Cover with buttered paper and a lid and put in a slow oven (325°) for approximately an hour. Remove the onion, stir the cabbage with a fork, and serve lightly piled up in a hot vegetable dish.

CAULIFLOWER CHEESE

INGREDIENTS

1 medium-sized cauliflower
½ to 1 oz. grated cheese,
    preferably Parmesan

½ pt cheese sauce
Parsley

METHOD

Cut the cauliflower into sprigs, taking each cut down to the base of the stalk so that each sprig terminates in a thin slice of stalk. Wash in salted water and drain. Boil in salted water for about 8 minutes but do not cook the vegetable until it is really soft. Drain well. Coat the bottom of a hot fireproof dish with cheese sauce and pile the sprigs on it in a neat shape. Pour the remaining sauce over the cauliflower, sprinkle with grated cheese, and brown under a hot grill. Garnish with parsley sprigs.

CARROTS CONSERVATIVE

INGREDIENTS

1 lb. carrots
1 teasp. sugar
Pepper and salt

¾ oz. butter
3 tablesps. water
Chopped parsley

METHOD

Scrape the carrots and slice very thinly. Place in a thick pan or in a casserole and add the sugar, pepper, salt, water, and fat. Cover with buttered paper and a lid and cook in a slow heat or on top of the stove until tender. This will take 30 minutes to 1 hour depending on the thickness and age of the carrot slices. When they are tender, transfer to a hot vegetable dish and sprinkle with chopped parsley. Any liquid left in the pan should be served with the carrots. There should be about a tablespoonful left. If there is a lot more it can be evaporated over a flame before the carrots are served.

CARROTS VICHY

INGREDIENTS

1 lb. carrots	Vichy water
¾ oz. butter	Pepper and salt
1 teasp. sugar	Chopped parsley

METHOD

Scrape the carrots and cut into slices one-eighth of an inch thick. Place in a thick pan and add pepper, salt, sugar, and fat. Barely cover with Vichy water. Bring to the boil and skim. Cover with a lid and simmer gently until tender. Serve on a hot vegetable dish and garnish with chopped parsley.

CHICORY STEWED IN BUTTER

This recipe is equally good with sea-kale or leeks in place of chicory.

INGREDIENTS

1 lb. chicory	2 oz. fried bacon or ham cut
2 oz. butter	into dice
1 teasp. lemon juice	Chopped parsley
Pepper and salt	

METHOD

Remove bruised leaves from the chicory and prise out the core at the stalk end with the point of a knife. Cut the heads across into slices one inch thick. Melt the butter in a shallow but thick pan and add the chicory (a shallow pan is required so that the chicory is spread over the base in a thin layer). Turn it over for a few moments in the fat and then season with pepper and salt. Cover with buttered paper and a closely fitting lid and cook over a very slow flame for 10–15 minutes or until tender. The vegetable should not be completely soft when it is served. Stir in a teaspoonful of lemon juice (or more if required) and two ounces diced, fried lean bacon or ham. Pile in a hot vegetable dish and sprinkle with chopped parsley. Ham can be omitted from this recipe.

COURGETTES

Courgettes or baby marrows are delicious if they are well seasoned and cooked or garnished with herbs or a well-flavoured sauce. They can easily taste insipid if boiled. Braising is an excellent method of cooking and the recipe for braised celery can be used for courgettes. Another satisfactory way of cooking them is to sauté them.

COURGETTES AND BROWNED BUTTER

Wipe one pound of courgettes. If they are very small they can be left whole, but if preferred they can be sliced lengthwise in one-inch slices. Put them in a thick pan with three-quarters of an ounce of butter and season with pepper and salt. Cover with buttered paper and a lid, and cook very slowly until clear. This will take about 10 minutes. Lift on to a hot vegetable dish and pour browned butter over them.

BROWNED BUTTER

Fry one and a half ounces of butter until nut-brown. Remove
from the stove and add one and a half tablespoons of tarragon
vinegar and one tablespoon of chopped fresh herbs. Season
with pepper and salt. Parsley, thyme, marjoram, and tarragon are a good combination, but other blends of herbs can
be selected. Fennel and chives are both suitable additions.

COURGETTES AND ONIONS

Take equal weights of onions and courgettes. Peel and slice
the onions but leave the courgettes whole. Place them in a
thick pan. Add olive oil in the proportion of two tablespoons
of oil to every pound of mixed vegetables. Add pepper and
salt, cover with a lid and simmer slowly for an hour. Serve
in a vegetable dish with chopped parsley as a garnish.

CELERIAC

The turnip-rooted celery has a fine flavour and can be
shredded as finely as tobacco and served raw in salads or can
be cooked and served in many ways.

CREAMED CELERIAC

INGREDIENTS

1 lb. celeriac   *Chopped parsley*
1–2 oz. margarine or butter   *3–4 tablesps. cream*
Pepper and salt

METHOD

Peel the celeriac, cut into wedge-shaped pieces or dice, and
drop into boiling salted water. Boil for 5 minutes, drain, and
run cold water through the vegetable. Place the pieces in a
thick pan containing one to two ounces of melted fat and

allow them to colour slightly on one side. Turn with a spoon and colour on the other side. Season well and cover with a lid. Lower the heat and continue to cook for about 20 minutes or until tender. Just before they are done, add a little cream and more butter. Pile on to a hot serving dish and sprinkle with chopped parsley.

CELERIAC AUX FINES HERBES is cooked in the same way but cream is omitted, and instead of parsley alone the vegetable is sprinkled with chopped tarragon, chervil, and parsley mixed together.

CREAMED SPINACH

INGREDIENTS

1 lb. spinach
Salt, pepper, and grated
    nutmeg

½ oz. butter
1–2 tablesps. cream

METHOD

Wash the spinach in several waters until free from soil. Drain and remove large midribs and bruised leaves. Place into a dry pan and add a pinch of salt. Cover with a lid and place the pan over a moderate flame. Cook the spinach for 7 minutes. Drain well, pressing out water with a plate. Rub through a sieve or cream in an electric blender. Replace the spinach in the pan and season with pepper, salt, and grated nutmeg. Stir until hot, add the fat and cream, and stir until well blended. Serve on a slice of toasted bread in a hot vegetable dish. White sauce can be used in place of cream.

Spinach purée makes a most attractive accompaniment and garnish to braised or roast lamb. If the purée is piled on slices of boiled turnip and garnished with pieces of hard-boiled egg white or with toasted almonds the croûtons can be arranged round the dish and used as a garnish.

CURRIED VEGETABLES

INGREDIENTS

Curry sauce (see recipe for
   curried meat)
1–1½ lb. diced vegetables
   including any or all of the
   following: carrot, turnip,
   celeriac, celery, peppers,
   aubergines, green or

broad beans, peas,
parsnips, tomatoes,
marrow, onions,
mushrooms, leeks,
cauliflower sprigs,
chicory, and sea-kale

METHOD

Prepare the sauce and bring to the boil. Add the vegetables
cut to approximately the same size and simmer gently until
done. Vegetables take much longer to cook in a curry sauce
than in water and therefore they can all be put in together.
Your friends and family can have sweet mango chutney and
poppadums with it.

FENNEL

Fennel is at its best eaten in salad. It is crisp and juicy and
delicious. The root and stem are used in salads and the
leaves are used as herbs.

    The root can be cooked in the same way as celery, so that
it can, for example, be boiled, braised, or served with cheese
sauce. It tends to be stringy when cooked and loses much
of its aromatic flavour.

    To boil fennel, first remove the tops and wash the root
in several waters. Drop it into fast-boiling salted water and
cook until tender. This will take 20 minutes or more according to size. Drain thoroughly and serve in a hot vegetable
dish. Pour melted butter or margarine over the fennel and
sprinkle with chopped parsley.

INDIAN STEW

INGREDIENTS

3 onions
3 large tomatoes
2 green peppers
6–8 oz. green peas or broad
   beans
1 green chilli

½ teasp. turmeric
½ teasp. allspice
3 cloves garlic
1 tablesp. lemon juice
Salt
2 tablesps. oil

METHOD

Peel and slice the onions and roll in turmeric and allspice.
Skin and slice the tomatoes. Cut the peppers into squares
and discard the seeds and stalk. Chop the garlic and chilli
and mix with the beans or peas and peppers. Put a layer of
onions in a casserole and cover with peppers. Add a layer
of tomatoes and sprinkle with salt. Continue adding layers
of peppers and tomatoes until the ingredients have all been
used up. Pour the oil over the vegetables, cover with a lid,
and stew slowly in an oven at 325° until cooked. Just before
serving, pour on the lemon juice.

MARROWS

Marrow can be boiled, steamed, or stuffed and roasted. Old
marrows should be parboiled or steamed for 7 minutes before
stuffing or roasting, or the outside will be dry and leathery.
Parboiled slices of marrow can be fried in shallow fat. The
flavour of marrow is not marked enough to stand dilution
during cooking, so that boiling tends to make it insipid.
Boiled marrow can be coated with white sauce or cheese
sauce, but still lacks flavour. A young marrow is delicious
cooked in the following way:

Take one small marrow and dice the flesh, including seeds; immature seeds are tender enough to eat. Melt three-quarters to one ounce of well-flavoured dripping in a pan and add to it a crushed clove of garlic. Add the marrow and toss over the heat until liquid begins to seep out of the flesh. Remove the garlic, add pepper and salt, cover with a lid, and simmer until tender. This will take about 15 minutes. Equal amounts of diced or sliced French or stringless beans previously boiled can be stirred into the marrow just before it is served.

PETITS POIS FRANÇAIS

For this dish to be perfect, it requires small French peas. In their absence, English ones do quite well.

INGREDIENTS

1 qt shelled peas	2 oz. spring onions
1 oz. butter	Pepper, salt, and 1 teasp.
1 oz. bacon (cut in strips	sugar
1 in. long and ¼ in. wide)	¼ oz. flour
A small lettuce	

METHOD

Place the peas in a thick saucepan and add the sugar, bacon, spring onions (peeled but left whole), and lettuce cut into thin shreds. Season with salt and pepper, barely cover with water and add half an ounce of fat. Cover with a lid and simmer gently until tender. This will take approximately an hour. Cream the remaining butter with the flour and stir this gradually into the pan, and continue to stir until the thickened sauce has boiled for at least a minute. The mixture should be fairly thick. Correct the seasoning before serving in a hot vegetable dish.

There are many slight variations to this recipe. Bacon is

not always included and flour is sometimes omitted. If flour is not used the fat is all put in at once and only two or three tablespoons of water are added. This should reduce considerably in volume during cooking.

PETITS POIS ST CLOUD

Use the previous recipe and add two ounces of new carrots sliced into thin rings. Add these when cooking begins.

RATATOUILLE

INGREDIENTS

2 *large onions*	*Salt*
6 *medium-sized tomatoes*	*Pinch of thyme*
1 *green pepper*	*A bay leaf* } *in muslin*
½ *fairly small marrow*	6 *peppercorns*
2 *tablesps. oil*	

METHOD

Prepare all the vegetables, slicing the onion and dicing the remainder. Cook the onions very gently in oil for 10 minutes until they become clear. Add the remaining vegetables, herbs, and seasoning. Cook over a very slow heat for 2 hours, with a lid on the pan. Remove the herbs and pour the vegetables into a hot dish. Sufficient liquid comes from the vegetables to moisten this dish. Celery or celeriac can be added to ratatouille and there are some who consider it incomplete without aubergine in as well. It is improved if chopped parsley is sprinkled over the top when it is served.

RED CABBAGE

Red cabbage can be boiled in salted water in the same way as green cabbage. It becomes pale in colour but has a good flavour. It takes longer to cook than green cabbage. The colour is deeper and the flavour is excellent if it is cooked in the following way:

INGREDIENTS

1 medium-sized red cabbage
1 oz. butter, margarine, or
   tablesp. oil
1–2 tablesps. black treacle
1 large cooking apple, peeled
   and sliced

1 onion, grated or chopped
1 tablesp. lemon juice
⅛ pt red wine
Salt and pepper

METHOD

Cut the cabbage into quarters and remove the hard stalk. Shred across into thin strips. Soak these in cold water for 1 hour and then drain. Place the fat or oil in a thick pan and add the onion. Cook gently until clear but not brown. Add the remaining ingredients and cook very slowly for 2 hours, with a lid on the pan.

The quantity of treacle and lemon juice added can be varied to suit individual taste. Six crushed juniper berries can be cooked with the cabbage and are usually added if it is to be served with pheasant.

SAUERKRAUT

Sauerkraut hails from Germany and is made from solid white cabbage. It is prepared by putting a layer of shredded cabbage in a particular type of wooden tub and sprinkling the cabbage with salt and some caraway seeds (optional). These layers are repeated until the tub is full and then the whole mass is pressed closely together. The outer leaves of the cabbage are used to cover the top layer of shreds and salt is sprinkled on these. A small amount of water is put in the tub and a cloth is laid over the top. A wooden lid which is small enough to clear the rim of the tub is put on last of all and a heavy weight is placed on the lid so that the cabbage is under pressure. After about three to four weeks, fermentation has taken place and the sauerkraut is ready for use. It is necessary to turn the cabbage every few days or at least once a week during the fermentation period. It should be quite white if properly fermented.

It is usual in this country to buy prepared sauerkraut though it can be made at home in small quantities in an earthenware vessel. It should be washed very well before use.

To cook sauerkraut take one pound of sauerkraut and wash it well. Put into boiling salted water or stock and boil for 30–40 minutes. Drain in a colander, return to the hot pan, and reheat with about one ounce of butter. Stir in a generous amount of freshly milled pepper before serving.

Sauerkraut is served with pork more frequently than with other meats, but in Germany it also accompanies Frankfurter sausages and all manner of meat, poultry, game, and fish.

SPINACH SOUFFLÉ

INGREDIENTS

2 lb. spinach	4 eggs
2 oz. butter	Grated nutmeg
1½ oz. flour	Salt and cayenne pepper
½ pt milk	Watercress

METHOD

Wash the spinach and put in a covered pan with a pinch of salt and boil for 7 minutes. Drain well and chop finely. Rub through a sieve or pulp it in an electric blender. Melt the butter in a pan of three to four pints capacity. Add the flour and cook until of a sandy texture but not browned. Gradually work in the milk and then stir until boiling. Remove from the stove and stir in salt, nutmeg, and a little cayenne pepper. Beat the egg yolks and gradually pour some of the hot sauce on to them. Mix well and return to the saucepan. Stir thoroughly and stir in the spinach purée. Whisk the egg whites until stiff enough to hold peaks and transfer them to the saucepan. Fold them carefully into the spinach mixture, using a metal spoon and mixing with a cutting action. Pour the mixture into a prepared soufflé case and bake in an oven at 425° for 30–35 minutes. If the top becomes very brown lower the heat to 375° and allow extra baking time. The soufflé is done when the centre is set. A steel skewer inserted in the centre will come out clean. Serve immediately on a dish mat on an entrée dish and garnish with watercress.

TOMATOES PROVENÇALE

INGREDIENTS

1 lb. tomatoes
¾ lb. onions
1 clove garlic
1½ oz. dripping, butter, or
    margarine

1 oz. breadcrumbs
1 tablesp. chopped parsley
Pepper and salt

METHOD

Skin the tomatoes and cut into slices. Peel the onions and slice very thinly. Chop the garlic. Place one ounce of fat in a thick pan, add the garlic and onions and cover with a lid. Cook gently for 15 minutes or longer, until the onions are clear. Stir in the chopped parsley and season with pepper and salt. Grease a fireproof dish and put a layer of onion in the base, cover with sliced tomato and season with pepper and salt. Repeat until all the vegetables are used. Sprinkle the surface with breadcrumbs and add the remaining fat cut into small pieces. Bake in a moderately hot oven (375°) for 20–30 minutes.

If only a faint flavour of garlic is desired the whole crushed clove can be put in the pan and removed again before the parsley is added.

CHAPTER 10

Sweets

THERE are two possible attitudes you can take towards sweets, and they are equally satisfactory. You can either make ordinary sweets for your family or guests, whilst you stick to fresh fruit, or something savoury like cheese. Or you can make sweets with as little carbohydrate as possible, and join in with the others, though perhaps with a smaller portion. Most likely, you will do both at different times, so that for example you have the sweet on special party occasions but otherwise keep to savouries.

The recipes have been chosen so as to contain the minimal amounts of starch. Wherever possible, too, we have given you the alternative of using either sugar or some sugarless substitute like saccharine. Some people find that saccharine has an unattractive after-taste, which they do not find with preparations like Saxin.

Sometimes, you will find it difficult or impossible to avoid sugar altogether. Thus, you cannot possibly make meringue without sugar, so this is an example where you must use your discretion, and see whether you can choose something else for yourself.

In general, your friends will not mind if your dishes are not very sweet. More particularly, you and your family will begin to appreciate better the taste of such foods as fruit when they are not too sweet.

*

APPLE POLONAISE

INGREDIENTS

1¼ lb. apple
Apricot jam

2 egg whites
1 oz. sugar } for meringue

METHOD

Peel and core the apples and cut them into slices about quarter of an inch thick. Butter a fireproof dish and put a layer of apple slices on the bottom. Spread sparingly with apricot jam. Put more apple slices on top and spread with jam, and continue until the apples are used up. Cover with a sheet of greased paper and bake in a slow oven (325°) until absolutely tender. The time taken depends on the type of apple used. When the apples are soft, remove them from the oven and turn the heat up to 375°. Whisk the egg whites until they form peaks, and then beat in the sugar a little at a time. Pile this meringue on top of the apples and return to the oven to colour to a pale brown. This requires about 5 minutes. A little grated coconut can be sprinkled over the top of the meringue before it is put in the oven.

Note: Saccharine and Saxin will not make a meringue. Sugar must be used for this purpose.

AVOCADO PEAR

2 portions

Halve a pear, remove the stone, brush the cut surface with lemon juice. Sprinkle a little sugar in the cavity in the centre and serve with cream if required.

BAKED APPLES

INGREDIENTS: 4 portions

4 apples
¾ oz. butter
2 oz. dried fruit

Sweetening agent, or
    1 tablesp. honey or syrup

METHOD

Remove a slice from the top of each apple and scoop out the
core with a teaspoon. Fill the centre with chopped sultanas,
chopped dates, chopped ginger, or glacé pineapple. Put a
small piece of fat on top of the fruit and replace the circle
cut from the top of each apple. Place the fruit in a fireproof
dish. Mix the sweetening agent with about six tablespoons
of water and pour it round the apples. Cover with greased
paper and bake in an oven at 350° until completely tender.

BAKED ORANGES

INGREDIENTS: 4 portions

4 whole oranges (choose a
    sweet variety with thin
    skins)
4 teasps. butter
Sweetening agent, or
    4 tablesps. sugar

Water
Cornflour
Orange juice
A few drops of Curaçao

METHOD

Place the oranges in a saucepan, cover with water, and put
on a lid. Boil gently for 30 minutes and then leave in the pan
until cold. Cut a slice off the stalk end of each fruit and
remove the core and pips but leave the pulp. Place a quarter
of the sweetening agent and a teaspoon of butter in each
orange and replace the slice on top. Pack closely together in

a casserole and add enough of the cooking water from the saucepan to come less than half-way up the side of the casserole. Put on a tightly fitting lid and bake in an oven at 375° for 1½–2 hours – if you can leave them longer they are even better.

At the end of this time transfer the fruits to a hot serving dish and measure the cooking water. To every half-pint cooking water allow one-eighth of a pint of orange juice and half a level tablespoonful of cornflour. Blend the cornflour with the orange juice and then stir in the cooking liquid. Stir until boiling and add a few drops of Curaçao. Pour this over the oranges and serve with cream.

BAKED PINEAPPLE PUDDING

INGREDIENTS: 3–4 portions

1 small tin pineapple	Sweetening agent, or
2 eggs	1½ oz. sugar
1½ oz. flour	¾ pt milk (or less)
1½ oz. butter	3 teasps. sugar for meringue

METHOD

Drain the fruit and cut it into small pieces. Melt the butter in a saucepan and add the flour. Cook together until of a sandy texture but not coloured. Gradually work in most of the milk and stir until boiling. Add the sweetener and more milk if necessary to give a coating consistency. Remove from the heat and cool slightly. Add the beaten egg yolks and mix well and then reheat gently. Stir in the fruit and transfer the mixture to a greased baking dish. Whip the egg whites until they form soft peaks and then beat in three teaspoons of sugar. Pile this meringue on top of the pineapple mixture and bake in an oven at 375° until the meringue is golden brown. This will take 6–10 minutes.

BAVAROISE

INGREDIENTS: 4 portions

¼ oz. custard powder
1½ eggs
Sweetening agent, or
  2 oz. sugar
½ pt milk
¼ pt cream for whipping

¼ teasp. vanilla essence
½ oz. gelatine
4 tablesps. water
Whipped cream for
  decoration

METHOD

Put the gelatine in a small basin and add the cold water. Stand for 5 minutes and then heat in a pan of hot water until all the gelatine crystals have dissolved. Blend the milk, sweetener, and custard powder and stir until boiling. Cool slightly and pour on to the beaten egg yolks. Reheat over a flame until the mixture coats the back of a spoon but do not allow to boil. Add the vanilla essence and strain into a basin. Strain in the dissolved gelatine and continue to stir the mixture until it is quite cold. Whip the cream until it just begins to thicken and fold it carefully into the custard. Pour the Bavaroise mixture into a mould and leave it in a cold place until set. Dip the mould into hot water and turn on to a glass dish. Decorate with whipped cream.

CHOCOLATE BAVAROISE is made from the same recipe with half an ounce of cocoa powder added. This should be blended with the sweetener and custard powder. More sweetener will be necessary when cocoa is used.

RASPBERRY OR STRAWBERRY BAVAROISE is made by adding an eighth of a pint of sieved fruit to the custard mixture before it is cooled. Fresh fruit gives the best flavour but frozen or tinned fruit can be used. Vanilla essence is omitted in a fruit Bavaroise.

CARAMEL CUSTARD

6 portions

The caramel which tops caramel custard is made from four ounces of sugar, but very little of this is used to line the moulds. The remainder is served separately as a sauce, and can always be refused.

CARAMEL INGREDIENTS

4 oz. sugar	2 or 3 drops lemon juice
1/8 pt. water	

CUSTARD INGREDIENTS

4 eggs	Sweetening agent, or
1 pt milk	1 1/2 oz. sugar
Vanilla flavouring	

METHOD

Grease twelve small dariole moulds. Place the sugar in a thick pan and add the water and lemon juice. Heat very slowly indeed without stirring until the sugar crystals have dissolved, and then turn up the flame. Stir until the syrup is golden brown. Remove from the heat *at once* and pour a very thin layer into the bottom of each mould. Add an eighth of a pint of water to any syrup remaining in the pan and leave it in a warm place until the caramel dissolves. Serve this in a sauce-boat. Whisk the eggs and vanilla essence slightly. Warm the milk and sweetener to blood heat and pour on to the eggs. Strain into a jug and fill each mould with custard.

Stand the moulds in a dripping tin containing sufficient water to come nearly to the top of each mould. Place in an oven at 350° until set. This will take approximately 30 minutes. To test if the custard is done, insert a pointed knife to the base of one mould and when it is cooked the caramel will float to the top. Remove from the oven and cool overnight, preferably in a refrigerator. Turn into a glass dish and serve the sauce separately.

CHOCOLATE AND RATAFIA JELLY

INGREDIENTS: 4–5 portions

1 *lemon jelly square*	*Sweetening agent or* 1½ *oz.*
½ *oz. cocoa*	*sugar*
¾ *pt boiling water*	*Vanilla essence*
¼ *pt unsweetened*	*Ratafia biscuits*
evaporated milk	

METHOD

Pour half a pint of boiling water on to the jelly square and stir until dissolved. Pour quarter of a pint of water on to the cocoa and sweetener and mix well. Allow both to get cold. Add the vanilla and evaporated milk to the cocoa mixture and then pour all of this into the jelly. When the liquid is completely cold but not setting, whip it vigorously. Do not pause until it forms a light foam which is so viscous that a little of it run from the tip of the whisk will leave a train on the surface of the mixture. Pour it into a serving dish and chill. Decorate the edge with ratafia biscuits.

CHOCOLATE SOUFFLÉ (HOT)

INGREDIENTS: 4 portions

2 *oz. flour*	½ *oz. cocoa powder*
2 *oz. butter*	½ *pt milk*
Sweetening agents, or	*Vanilla essence*
2 *oz. sugar*	3 *small or* 2 *very large eggs*

METHOD

Melt the butter in a pan of three to four pints capacity. Stir in the flour and cook until of a sandy texture but not coloured. Blend the cocoa and milk and work this gradually into the fat and flour. Stir until boiling. Cool slightly and pour on to the beaten egg yolks. Return to the pan and add vanilla essence and sweetener to taste. Whip the whites until they form soft peaks and fold the egg white carefully into the chocolate sauce, using a metal tablespoon. Transfer the mixture to a prepared soufflé case and bake for about 30 minutes in an oven at 425°. The soufflé is done when it is well risen and set in the centre. A steel skewer inserted into the centre will come out clean when the mixture is set.

CHOCOLATE SOUFFLÉ (COLD)

INGREDIENTS: 4 portions

7½ oz. cream for whipping
4 oz. plain block chocolate
2 tablesps. brandy or 1 tablesp. rum
Sweetening agent or 2½ oz. sugar
¼ oz. gelatine

3 eggs
3 tablesps. water
¼ teasp. vanilla essence
Whipped cream and chocolate vermicelli to decorate

METHOD

Put the gelatine into a small basin. Break the chocolate into pieces and put on top of the gelatine. Add four tablespoons of water and leave this to soak for 5 minutes. Then stand the basin in a pan of hot water until the chocolate is soft and the gelatine has dissolved. Whisk the egg yolks and sweetener until they are thick and pale in colour. Add the spirit to the chocolate mixture and stir this into the egg yolks with a metal tablespoon. Half whip the cream and fold this into the chocolate mixture. Whip the egg whites until they hold soft peaks and fold these into the soufflé. Pour the mixture into a prepared soufflé case and leave to set. Remove the paper band and decorate the edge with chocolate vermicelli and whipped cream.

CRANBERRY WHIP

INGREDIENTS: 3–4 portions

8 oz. tinned cranberries
  (sieved)
Sweetening agent or 3
  tablesps. sugar
3 tablesps. water
¼ oz. gelatine

3 egg whites
1 teasp. lemon juice
1 teasp. grated orange zest
Whipped cream for
  decoration

METHOD

Put the gelatine in a small basin, add the water, and soak for 5 minutes. Then stand the basin in a pan of hot water until the gelatine has dissolved. Stir the dissolved gelatine into the sieved cranberries and add sweetening and lemon juice. Beat the egg whites until they hold soft peaks and beat the orange zest into them. Fold the egg whites into the cranberry mixture with a metal tablespoon. Pour into a glass dish and leave to set. Decorate with whipped cream.

COFFEE SOUFFLÉ (HOT)

4 portions

Use the recipe and method given for chocolate soufflé (hot) but replacing the cocoa powder by two tablespoons of coffee essence. Alternatively, the soufflé can be made with quarter of a pint of milk and quarter of a pint of strong black coffee instead of half a pint of milk.

CURD PIE

3–4 portions

Curd tart is a popular sweet which is baked in a pastry case. The curd mixture can, however, be baked in a pie dish and served alone.

INGREDIENTS

1 pt milk	Grated zest and juice of
1 dessertsp. rennet	half a lemon
3 oz. butter	Sweetening agent or 3 oz.
2 eggs	sugar
2 oz. currants	Pinch of grated nutmeg

METHOD

Warm the milk to blood heat, stir in the rennet, and leave to stand until it forms a junket. Drain on a hair sieve.

Cream the fat and sweetener until pale, gradually beat in the eggs, lemon zest and juice, and the grated nutmeg. Stir in the curd and the currants. Spread into a greased baking dish and bake at 375° until set. It may be necessary to reduce the heat to 350° to prevent the surface browning too much. The curd requires 30–40 minutes in the oven.

FRUIT CREAMS

4–6 portions

Raw or cooked fruit can be used to make creams. It must be sieved through a nylon or hair sieve and sweetened to taste before being used. An electric blender will produce a satisfactory purée of apricots or peaches, but the fruits which contain small seeds, e.g. strawberries, raspberries, blackcurrants, and loganberries, should be sieved after blending. Frozen and canned fruit can also be used. Stewed, canned, and thawed frozen fruit should be drained on a sieve. Some juice is required with the creams but only the fruit itself should be made into a purée and all the juice measured separately.

INGREDIENTS

¼ pt custard	4 tablesps. water
¼ pt cream for whipping	½ oz. gelatine
¼ pt fruit purée	Jelly
⅛ pt fruit juice	Whipped cream

METHOD

Prepare the custard from a quarter pint of milk, one to one and a half ounces of sugar or equivalent sweetening agent, and either one egg or quarter of an ounce of custard powder. Stir continually until cold. Rub the fruit through a sieve and sweeten to taste. Half-whip the cream. Soak the gelatine in a basin with four tablespoons of water for 5 minutes and then stand the basin in a pan of hot water until the gelatine has dissolved. Pour a thin layer of jelly into the bottom of a one-pint mould or into six small dariole moulds and leave to set. Fold the fruit purée and juice into the cold custard and fold the cream into this mixture. Lastly, fold the dissolved gelatine. Fill each mould with the mixture and leave to set. Dip quickly into hot water and turn out into a glass dish. Decorate with whipped cream.

Instead of using whipped cream as a decoration the dish can be served with small pieces of cherry and angelica, or a zest of oranges and lemons arranged in a neat design in the layer of jelly used to line the mould.

ORANGE CREAMS

INGREDIENTS: 4–6 portions

¼ pt custard – see Fruit Creams	Rind of one orange
	½ oz. gelatine

¼ *pt cream for whipping*
The juice of 2 oranges plus
  enough bottled squash to
  give 8 fl. oz. of liquid

Whipped cream

METHOD

Grate the zest of one orange and squeeze the juice from two. Make the juice up to eight ounces with bottled squash. Make the custard and stir until cold. Soak the gelatine for 5 minutes in four tablespoons of the orange juice and then warm it over hot water until crystals dissolve. Half-whip the cream. Fold the orange juice and grated zest into the custard, fold in the cream and then the gelatine. Set in prepared moulds or in sundae glasses, or in empty orange rinds cut in halves. Decorate with whipped cream. If empty orange rinds are used, they should be scraped quite free from pith and each one should be balanced on a scone cutter or in a small basin so that it stands level before it is filled. The edge can be snipped with kitchen scissors into a series of regular points.

FRUIT FOOL

5–6 portions

Apricots, raspberries, blackcurrants, gooseberries, and plums are popular fruits for fool. Apple fool could be made but it is insipid in flavour. Some pale fruits such as rhubarb and gooseberries are improved by the addition of one or two drops of vegetable colouring. Raspberries and strawberries can be sieved and sweetened without previous cooking. A one-pound tin of fruit can be used in place of sweetened stewed fruit.

The consistency of a fool should be such that if a spoon is drawn over the surface the mark remains. It should not be so soft that it flows to a level surface. On the other hand, it should not be very stiff or it is unpleasant to eat.

INGREDIENTS

1–1 ½ lb. fruit	¼ pt custard
Sweetening agent or 4–6 oz. sugar	¼ pt cream for whipping

METHOD

Prepare the fruit and stew in a pan with a tablespoon of water. Have a tightly fitting lid on the pan and cook the fruit over a slow flame so that it does not burn. Once it begins to cook it will give out juice; if more water is added before it is cooked, the result will be too liquid to make a satisfactory fool. When it is cooked add the sweetening agent, strain the fruit, and reserve the juice. Rub the fruit through a nylon sieve or pulp it in an electric blender.

Make the custard with a quarter-ounce of custard powder, a quarter of a pint of milk, and sweetening agent or one ounce of sugar. Stir the fruit purée into the custard and leave to get cold. If the mixture is really thick when cold it can be diluted with some juice from the stewed fruit. Half-whip the cream, fold this into the fruit mixture with a tablespoon and pour into a glass dish or sundae glasses.

FRUIT SALAD IN MELON

INGREDIENTS: 4–5 portions

1 melon (watermelon is not suitable for this dish)	2 oz. strawberries or raspberries
1 dessert apple	2 oz. black grapes
1 dessert pear	A few drops of Kirsch, Maraschino, or Curaçao
1 peach	
1 orange	¼ pt cold syrup made with ¼ pt water and sweetener
¼ grapefruit	
2 oz. red cherries	

METHOD

Shave a thin slice of rind off the base of the melon so that it balances securely. Cut a slice off the top and remove the seeds. Use a vegetable scoop to remove as many balls of melon flesh as possible. Reserve these and scrape the rest of the flesh from the rind with a tablespoon to leave an empty case.

Peel and slice the apple, pear, and peach. Stone the cherries. Remove pips from the grapes. Cut the strawberries if they are too large to be served whole. Remove the rind from the orange and cut the flesh free from core and membranes or prepare it as a grapefruit is prepared for table. Prepare the grapefruit. Put all the fruits in a basin and moisten with a little cold syrup. Cover with a plate and chill in the refrigerator for 30 minutes. Stir in a few drops of liqueur. Drain the fruit and place it in the empty melon. Arrange a few pieces of fruit around the cut edge of the top of the melon and put vine leaves underneath it in a glass dish. As an alternative, the dry fruits can be arranged on a plate, sprinkled with sugar and liqueur, and left in a cold place for an hour. Drain them and put the fruit in the melon.

The fruits used in a salad vary according to season and availability. Pineapple, lichees, apricots, and other fruits can be included. Canned fruits can be added to a salad if fresh ones are out of season. The skin is frequently left on some or all of the black grapes to give colour to the salad. It is removed from white ones since grape skins are always tough to eat. The peel can be left on a red apple.

FRUIT SNOW

INGREDIENTS: 4 portions

1 lb. cooking apples	Sweetening agent or 4 oz.
Zest and juice of one lemon	sugar
2 egg whites	

METHOD

Make an incision all round the apples half-way down the side and bake in a moderate oven (350°) until cooked. Rub through a nylon sieve and stir in sweetener. Add the grated zest and juice of the lemon and allow the mixture to get quite cold. Beat the egg whites until quite stiff and add the pulp a teaspoonful at a time, whipping all the while.

Pile the apple snow into a glass dish or sundae glasses.

HONEYCOMB MOULD

INGREDIENTS: 4–5 portions

1 pt milk

Sweetening agent or 1½ oz. sugar

3 eggs

½ oz. gelatine

4 tablesps. water

Thin slice lemon zest or a few drops of any flavouring essence

A pinch of salt

METHOD

Infuse the lemon zest in the warm milk for 30 minutes. Beat the egg yolks slightly and add sweetener. Pour the warm milk on to the eggs and stir well. Return this mixture to the pan and stir over a slow heat until thick enough to coat the back of a spoon lightly. Add the salt. If lemon zest is used, remove it at this stage. If it is not used, add flavouring essence. Place the gelatine in a small basin and pour the water over it and allow it to stand for 5 minutes. Heat the basin in hot water until the gelatine dissolves and add this to the custard. Strain the custard into a basin and stir until cool and beginning to thicken. Whip the egg whites until they form soft peaks and fold them carefully into the custard with a metal spoon. Pour into a mould of one and a half pints capacity. When set, turn into a glass dish.

ICE CREAM (VANILLA)

INGREDIENTS: 8–10 portions

½ pt milk
½ pt cream whipping
3 egg yolks

1½ teasps. vanilla
Sweetening agent or 3 oz.
   sugar

If a decided flavour of vanilla is desired it may be necessary to use a good deal more than one and a half teaspoonfuls of essence.

METHOD

Make a thick custard of the egg yolks and milk, add sweetener and flavouring, and stir until cold. Whip the cream lightly and fold into the custard with a metal spoon. Freeze in an ice pail or in a refrigerator.

To make ice-cream in a refrigerator, set the thermostat on its coldest setting one hour in advance. Pour the ice-cream into an ice tray and put into the freezing compartment. When it is half-frozen tip it into a cold basin and whisk thoroughly. Return to the freezing compartment until nearly solid and then remove and whisk again. Return to the refrigerator until ready to serve.

New York ice-cream is made by whipping the egg whites until they form soft peaks and folding them into the custard and cream before freezing it.

Fruit ice-cream is made by folding together sweetened fruit purée and lightly whipped cream. The amount of fruit used depends on personal taste but up to equal quantities of purée and cream can be used.

The unfrozen mixture should taste very sweet because freezing causes it to appear much less sweet. Some recipes for ice-cream contain a little gelatine. This is added to reduce or prevent the formation of ice crystals in the mixture as it freezes.

JUNKET

INGREDIENTS: 4 portions

1 pt new milk
Sweetening agent or 1½ oz.
  sugar
2 teasps. rennet
Grated nutmeg

Flavouring essence or 1
  tablesp. rum or brandy
Whipped cream or
  Devonshire cream

METHOD

Put the sweetener and milk in a pan and warm to blood heat (100°–104°). Remove from the heat and stir in the rennet. Add flavouring or spirit and pour into a serving dish. Grate a little nutmeg over the top and leave in a warm place to set. Serve with whipped cream or Devonshire cream.

LEMON SNOW

INGREDIENTS: 4–5 portions

⅜ pt water (7½ fl. oz.)
¼ pt lemon juice
Sweetening agent or
  4 oz. sugar

Zest of one lemon
2 egg whites
½ oz. gelatine
Cherry and angelica

METHOD

Put the gelatine in a small pan and add the water. Soak for 5 minutes and then heat gently until the gelatine has dissolved. Remove from the heat and add the fruit juice, grated zest, and sweetener. Allow to get quite cold. Whip the egg whites until stiff and add the cold liquid a teaspoonful at a time, beating continuously. Beat until stiff. Pile into a serving dish, decorate with cherry and angelica, and chill before use.

MILANAISE SOUFFLÉ

INGREDIENTS: 6 portions

3 eggs
2 lemons
Sweetening agent or 4 oz. sugar
½ pt cream for whipping

½ oz. gelatine
5 tablesps. water
Chopped nuts, whipped cream, cherry, and angelica

METHOD

Soak the gelatine in water for 5 minutes and then warm over hot water until the crystals have dissolved. Separate the eggs. Grate the zest from the lemons and squeeze the juice. Whisk the egg yolks, sweetener, lemon juice, and grated zest in a bowl over a pan of hot water until thick and creamy. Remove from the heat and continue to whisk until the outside of the bowl is quite cold. The mixture must be stiff enough at this point to leave a trail on the surface when it runs from the whisk. Whip the cream lightly and fold it into the egg mixture with a metal tablespoon. Whip the whites until they form soft peaks and fold these in. Lastly, fold in the gelatine. Pour this mixture into a prepared soufflé case so that it comes about an inch up the paper projecting beyond the top of the case. Chill. When set remove the paper carefully and stand the soufflé case on a large plate. Toss chopped nuts against the side of the soufflé, using a teaspoon for the purpose. Decorate the top with whipped cream, cherries, and angelica and then place the soufflé case on a plate with a doily on it.

MILK JELLY

INGREDIENTS: 4 portions

1 pt milk
Small pieces of lemon zest or flavouring essence

½ oz. gelatine
Sweetening agent or 1 oz. sugar

METHOD

Put all the ingredients in a pan and soak for 5 minutes. Then place over a slow heat and stir until the gelatine has dissolved. Allow to cool, stirring occasionally. When cold, strain into a mould and chill in a refrigerator. Dip quickly into hot water and turn on to a serving dish.

For chocolate milk jelly, the same ingredients are used, but vanilla essence replaces the lemon rind. One and a half ounces of chocolate powder are also required. Mix the chocolate powder with half the milk and stir until boiling. Boil for one minute and then cool, stirring frequently to prevent the formation of a skin. Put the remaining ingredients in another pan and heat until the gelatine has dissolved. Remove from the flame and add the chocolate-flavoured milk.

It is important to allow a milk jelly to get cold and to stir it well just before it is poured into a mould. This prevents the cream rising to the top. Strain it into the mould, especially if it is a chocolate jelly where skin from the boiled milk may be present. An egg can be added to the jelly and is a valuable addition in invalid cookery. After the milk, sweetener, and gelatine have been warmed to dissolve the gelatine they should be poured on to a lightly beaten egg. The mixture is then returned to the pan and stirred over a slow heat until it thickens slightly. It must not boil. When it is cold, stir well and strain into a mould.

ORANGE FLUMMERY

INGREDIENTS: 4 portions

¾ pt water
1 oz. flour
¼ oz. gelatine
1 orange

2 tablesps. lemon juice
Angelica
Sweetening agent or 2½ oz. sugar

METHOD:

Blend the flour with a little of the water. Put the gelatine and sweetener in a pan and add the remaining water. Soak for 5 minutes and then stir over a slow heat until the gelatine has dissolved. Pour on to the blended flour and mix well. Return to the pan and stir until boiling. Simmer for 3 minutes.

Grate the zest of the orange and squeeze the juice. Add to this the lemon juice and then the flour mixture. Stir well and leave to become cool but not cold. Whisk until spongy and pour into a glass dish. Chill before serving. Decorate with angelica and small, thin pieces of orange zest cut into fancy shapes.

ORANGE MOUSSE

INGREDIENTS: 5–6 portions

¾ pt cream for whipping
Sweetening agent or 3½ to
    4 oz sugar.
1 tin of frozen
    orange concentrate
2 oranges

2 teasps. lemon juice
¾ oz. gelatine
5 tablesps. water
Whipped cream for
    decorating

METHOD

Soak the gelatine in water in a small basin for 5 minutes and then heat over hot water until dissolved. Grate the zest of the orange and squeeze the juice. Mix together the grated zest, orange, and lemon juice and orange concentrate. Whip the cream lightly, sweeten, and pour the fruit juice in, whisking all the time. Pour in the dissolved gelatine, still whisking. Pour the mixture into a serving dish and chill. Decorate with whipped cream.

ORANGE SOUFFLÉ

INGREDIENTS: 6 portions

Grated zest and juice of 2
   large oranges
Juice of half a lemon
3/8 pt cream for whipping
Sweetening agent or 3 oz.
   sugar

2 whole eggs and 1 egg
   white
1/2 oz. gelatine
Chopped nuts, whipped
   cream, cherries, and
   angelica

The orange and lemon juice should measure eight fluid
ounces. If the volume is less than this add bottled squash.

METHOD

Soak the gelatine in four tablespoons of fruit juice for 5
minutes and then warm over hot water until dissolved.
   Complete as for Milanaise soufflé.

ORANGE SNOW

INGREDIENTS: 4 portions

3/8 pt orange juice
1/8 pt water
Sweetening agent or 2 1/2 oz.
   sugar

1/2 oz. gelatine
Zest and juice of 1 orange
2 egg whites
Orange slices and angelica

METHOD

Grate the zest of the orange and squeeze the juice. Make the
juice up to half a pint with more fresh orange juice.
   Put the gelatine, sweetener, and water in a pan and soak
for 5 minutes. Then heat slowly until the gelatine has dissolved. Remove from the heat and stir in the orange juice
and grated zest. Allow to get quite cold. Whip the egg whites
until they form soft peaks and add the juice a teaspoonful

at a time, whisking continuously. Whisk until stiff and pile into a serving dish. Chill. Decorate with orange slices and angelica.

PEARS BAKED IN CIDER

INGREDIENTS: 6 portions

2 lb. stewing pears
Sweetening agent or 4 oz. sugar

Cider and water in equal quantities

METHOD

Peel the pears and leave them whole. Pack closely together in a casserole and add sweetener. Cover with cider and water and put on the lid. Place into an oven at 320° and stew gently for 6 hours. Remove the pears and place into a glass dish. Boil the syrup until it is reduced to about half its volume. Pour this over the pears. Serve cold, with cream.

This is a dish which can be left to cook overnight in a very slow oven. The long, slow cooking renders the whole pear soft and edible.

PRUNE MOUSSE

INGREDIENTS: 4 portions

1 jelly square
2–3 tablesps. sherry
6 oz. prunes

Sweetening agent or 1½ oz. sugar
Boiling water

METHOD

Cover the prunes with boiling water and simmer until tender. Add sweetener. Pour off the cooking water and use it to dissolve the jelly square. The total volume (liquid and jelly square) should be seven-eighths of a pint. Put the prunes through a nylon sieve. Allow the jelly to get quite cold but not set and then whisk vigorously until a thick foam is produced. Add the sieved prune, a teaspoonful at a time, whisking constantly. Add the sherry last of all and whisk until setting. Pour into a glass dish and chill before serving.

A tin of strained prunes (sold as a baby food) can replace the prunes and sweetening in this recipe. In this case, the jelly square should be dissolved in boiling water to give a total volume of eighteen fluid ounces.

STRAWBERRY MOUSSE

INGREDIENTS: 6–8 portions

1 lb. fresh strawberries or 1 lb. frozen jam strawberries
Sweetening agent or 3 oz. sugar
1–2 teasps. lemon juice
¾ pt cream for whipping
¾ oz. gelatine
6 tablesps. water
Red colouring if required
Whipped cream for decoration

METHOD

Put the sweetener and lemon juice into a basin and rub the strawberries through a nylon sieve on to them. Stir until sweetening dissolves.

Soak the gelatine in water for 5 minutes and then warm over hot water until dissolved.

Whip the cream lightly and pour the strawberry mixture slowly into it, continuing to whip meanwhile. Pour in the dissolved gelatine, still whipping. Add one or two drops of colouring if necessary.

Pour into a glass dish or into a mould and chill before serving. Decorate with whipped cream and small strawberries.

If jam strawberries are not available a twelve-ounce packet of frozen strawberries can be used instead. These are sweetened, so that no further sweetening agent is required. There is no need to alter the proportions of the other ingredients in the recipe, but a drop of strawberry essence may be required.

SWEDISH APPLE

INGREDIENTS: 3–4 portions

1 lb. cooking apples
Sweetening agent or 3 oz.
  sugar

¼ pt cream for whipping
Crushed cornflakes
½ oz. butter

METHOD

Cut a slit round the circumference of each apple, half-way down the side. Bake in a moderate oven (375°) until tender.

Put sweetener into a basin and sieve the apples on to it through a nylon sieve. Stir until sweetener dissolves and then leave until cold.

Place in a serving dish. Lightly whip the cream and pile or pipe it on top of the fruit.

Melt the butter in a pan. Turn the crushed cornflakes in this mixture until crisp. Cool them on soft paper and then sprinkle on top of the cream. Cornflakes alone also make a good topping.

Apricot purée can be used in place of apple.

SOUFFLÉ OMELET

INGREDIENTS: 1–2 portions

2 eggs
Sweetening agent or 1 teasp.
  sugar

A little clarified butter
Fruit purée

METHOD

Put quarter of an ounce of butter in a seven-inch omelet pan and heat until it melts. Remove the sediment and froth with a spoon. Swill the remaining oil round the pan so that the whole surface is greasy. Pour away any surplus.

Separate the eggs and whisk the yolks with sweetening agent until pale in colour and very thick. Use a basin of about one and half pints capacity so that there is room in it for the whipped whites to be added.

Whip the whites until they form soft peaks and transfer them to the basin containing the yolks. Carefully fold together with a metal spoon.

Pour the mixture into the hot omelet pan and cook gently until golden brown on the underside. Place under a moderate grill until the top is golden brown and the omelet has risen well and set in the centre. Alternatively, put the omelet pan in a moderate oven (400°) until the eggs have set.

Have a sheet of paper sprinkled with sugar on the table and invert the omelet on to this. Make a cut across the centre of the base, spread with warm sieved fruit, and fold in two.

Serve on a hot plate.

SYLLABUB

Syllabub is a name which calls to mind by-gone days when time and ingredients were in ample supply. It is rarely made today but there is no reason why it should disappear from the table.

Two recipes are given here, one rather less extravagant than the other.

INGREDIENTS (RECIPE 1)

½ pt sherry
Thinly pared zest of 1 lemon
¾ pt cream for whipping

Sugar or sweetener to taste
1 tablesp. brandy

METHOD

Place the lemon zest in a bottle and add the sherry. Cork the bottle and leave it overnight. Next day, strain off the sherry and add to it the remaining ingredients. Whisk together by hand or in an electric mixer. Skim off the froth as it forms and drain it on a nylon sieve for 3 hours. Pile into serving glasses.

INGREDIENTS (RECIPE 2)

½ pt sherry or white wine   *Lemon zest and sweetening*
  or Madeira   *as above*
½ *pt cream*

METHOD

As above.

Lemon juice and orange juice can be used to replace part of the wine in a syllabub. A little powdered cinnamon is sometimes added when white wine is used. Cinnamon flavour blends well with lemon but not so happily with orange.

Some old recipes for syllabub give instructions for the serving glasses to be half filled with wine and the whipped cream to be spooned on top.

VANILLA CREAMS

INGREDIENTS: 2–3 portions

¼ pt custard   ¼ *oz. gelatine*
¼ *pt cream for whipping*   *Lemon jelly*
2 *tablesps. water*   *Cherries and angelica*
Vanilla pod or essence

METHOD

Place the vanilla pod in a pan, add the milk, and warm to blood heat. Leave for 30 minutes and then strain. Use the milk to make custard (see fruit creams). Stir the custard until cold.

Pour a thin layer of jelly into the base of six dariole moulds and leave to set. Arrange a decoration on the jelly, using cherries and angelica cut into small pieces. Add a little more cold jelly and leave this to set. (One large mould can be used instead of six small ones.)

Soak the gelatine in cold water for 5 minutes and then warm over hot water until dissolved.

Whip the cream lightly and fold it into the cold custard. Fold in the gelatine and pour the mixture into the prepared moulds. Leave to set and then dip quickly into hot water and turn on to a serving dish.

If a vanilla pod is not used, vanilla essence should be added to the custard when it is removed from the heat.

WINE JELLY

INGREDIENTS: 6–8 portions

1 ¼ pts water	3 cloves
½ pt sherry	Sweetener or 3 oz. sugar
¼ pt lemon juice	1 oz. gelatine
Grated zest of 2 lemons	Whites and shells of 2 eggs
1 in. cinnamon stick	

METHOD

Crush the egg-shells and put them into a large pan. Add all the other ingredients and leave to soak for 5 minutes, then stir over a slow heat until the gelatine has dissolved. Whisk vigorously until a froth develops. Stop whisking and allow the liquid to boil rapidly for half a minute. Draw the pan off the flame and allow the jelly to settle. Strain through a tammy cloth and pour into a mould. Leave to set. Dip quickly into hot water and turn into a serving dish.

YOGHOURT

2 portions

Yoghourt makes a delicious and inexpensive sweet. To one carton of yoghourt add sweetener and sufficient fresh raspberries or chopped dessert apple to give a good flavour. Mix well, chill in a refrigerator, and serve with whipped cream.

Chopped nuts can be used to decorate yoghourt with apple in it. Other fruits can, of course, be used to suit individual preference.

The exact amount of sweetening required depends upon the palate of each person and upon the fruit used.

ZABAGLIONE

INGREDIENTS: 4–6 portions

8 egg yolks   Sweetening agent or 1 oz.
6 tablesps. Marsala or sweet   caster sugar
   white wine

METHOD

Put all the ingredients into a very thick enamel-lined pan or into a bowl resting on a pan of warm water. Whisk for a few moments off the heat and then put the pan over a low flame. Continue to whisk until the volume has increased four-fold and the mixture is thick enough to hold its shape. It must never boil.

Serve in small tepid glasses. Macaroons are generally served with zabaglione.

There are recipes which include a pinch of powdered cinnamon, but a good wine does not call for it.

CHAPTER 11

Packed Meals

YOU can think of packed meals in terms of one of those beautiful – and huge – French paintings, with large wicker baskets overflowing with pheasants and joints of meat and luscious pies and masses of fruit and flasks of wine. Or you can think of a tough workman carrying a small tin, the contents of which you may guess to be a couple of cheese sandwiches and a Cornish pasty. In fact, you will find nowadays much less difference in the sorts of meals people take out with them. Very many foods are available all through the year, where not so long ago there would be a restricted season, often quite short. Moreover, there are many new sorts of foods, and new ways in which they have been prepared, and above all many of them are within the reach of most of us. So the choice of foods which can be packed is very large, and there need be no vast difference in the sorts of foods packed for lunch at work, or a day at Southend, or an afternoon at Ascot. But, of course, there is a difference between a party picnic and a box for the office or factory. So, here, are some of the party pieces.

Of course, if you are having something like a barbecue and cooking out of doors, it is quite easy to arrange for meals without much carbohydrate. Better still, they can be arranged with carbohydrate foods like bread or sweet drinks for those who want them. Salads will in any case be expected, and your main dish will be based on chops, steaks, or sausages. You can make fancier dishes, too, like kebab and most of the work in preparing these can be done indoors.

If you are packing completely prepared dishes, you

will find that there are nowadays tremendously helpful packings and packing materials. All of these will make packing easier; some of them will allow you to carry dishes which can make the difference between a snack and a party. Think, for example, of the sorts of things you can carry in vacuum flasks, and remember that you can get wide-mouthed flasks as well as the commoner ones with narrow mouths. Hot soups, grilled sausages, curries, and stews – you can think of lots more yourself. It is important, though, to put these foods into the vacuum flask when they are really hot. You should also not leave them in for more than a few hours; anything you bring home should be taken out and reheated. Some people also forget that vacuum flasks will keep cold foods cold as well as hot foods hot. If you are going to serve salmon mayonnaise on a really hot day, it makes all the difference if the salmon mayonnaise and your salad are all really cold and crisp.

Other useful packages can be made with waxed cartons, screw-top plastic or glass jars, and some of the containers used in the refrigerator or oven. It is worth just that amount more care and trouble to bring some oil and vinegar for your salad, horseradish for your beef, mint for your lamb. In addition, there are plastic bags and wrappings, and aluminium foil. With these you can easily pack fish-cakes, roast poultry, cold meats, and tongue, and salads of all sorts.

With all these ways of packing and carrying, it is perhaps necessary to remember that there are still the tinned foods where the manufacturer has already gone to the trouble of preparing and packing for you. Here it is worth checking from time to time, because more and more exciting things are appearing constantly.

Finally, look out for some of the new dehydrated foods and meals. These, too, are increasing in variety almost every day, and provide excellent handy dishes.

Now we turn to the more mundane, day-to-day packed

meals which we might need for example to take to work. If you are lucky, you may be able to eat your meal with knife, fork, and plate. There is then a wide variety of dishes you can prepare, just like the ones mentioned earlier in this book. It is a little more difficult if the meal has to be eaten entirely with the fingers where one thinks automatically in terms of sandwiches. You can, if you wish, make sandwiches with scooped-out bread-rolls or with starch-reduced crispbread. But there are many items which can be made very well without any bread at all.

Here are some examples. Some of them are obvious, like the leg or wing of a chicken, or cold sausages, or hard-boiled eggs. Other examples, however, are perhaps not quite so obvious.

1. Thin slices of ham or cold meat, wrapped round a finger of melon.

2. Lettuce leaves wrapped round sticks of cheese or hard herring roes.

3. Sausages split lengthwise and filled with thin slices of cheese, or with mayonnaise and chopped vegetables.

4. Cold kebab. There is a wide variety of foods, and mixtures of foods, which can be put on to a cocktail stick. Diced meats and fruits go well together. Some other suitable combinations are:

Cheese and pineapple; pork and pineapple; luncheon meat and cherries; ham and veal; mutton and prunes; cold beef and gherkins; galantine and bath chap; sausage and prunes; sausage and red or green peppers; prawns and mushrooms; anchovy fillets and broad beans. It is a good idea to take as well either some crisp salad in a plastic bag, or an apple or pear or some other fruit.

5. Filled celery. Short lengths of celery stalks can be filled with cream cheese, or grated cheddar cheese with mayonnaise, or tinned fish, mashed and seasoned, or potted

meat or scrambled egg. If the celery stalks are put together, they are easy to handle and not at all messy.

6. Filled cucumber. Much the same can be done with short lengths of cucumber, cut lengthwise in two. A great deal of the pulp, however, must be removed in order to leave room for the filling.

7. Scotch eggs.

8. Stuffed hard-boiled eggs. Here again a wide variety of stuffings is possible, including meat paste or fish paste or simply egg yolks seasoned and mixed with mayonnaise.

9. Meat or fish croquettes. These can be made from sausage meat, or from any cooked meat or fish. It is important that they should be well seasoned, otherwise they are rather insipid when cold. For this reason, smoked haddock or kipper are good. If you use other fish, or meat, add quite liberal amounts of pepper and salt. To make the croquettes, mince the fish or meat finely, and moisten with a little egg. Shape and dip into beaten egg and a little bread raspings, and fry in deep fat until golden brown.

All of the foods mentioned can be eaten with the fingers. Naturally, variety can be considerably extended if one or more of the snacks can be taken in small plastic or cardboard containers, and eaten with fork or spoon.

FORK SNACKS

1. Russian salads. If these are made with generous portions of meat or fish, they form a substantial course.

2. Cottage cheese with herbs or nuts, or chopped gherkins, peppers, tomatoes, and capers.

3. Meat or fish in aspic with chopped vegetables.

4. Ham or salmon mousse.

SANDWICH FILLINGS

In addition to some of these snacks there are many sorts of fillings for the scooped-out rolls or starch-reduced crispbread.

Some of them are well enough seasoned or flavoured in themselves. This is true, for example, of liver paste or cod's roe paste. For other fillings, it makes all the difference if a little trouble is taken in flavouring. Cold beef is good in a sandwich; with a little horseradish sauce, it is very much better. Here are some other suggestions, some obvious, some less so:

Mutton with mint; ham with mustard; salami with olives; brawn with French mustard; soft cheese with chopped celery, grated apple, or chopped nuts, or pickles or chutney; prawns with mayonnaise; sandwich spread with chopped meat or eggs; sardines with chopped watercress; smoked haddock with chopped cooked mushroom; flaked kipper with chopped tomato; flaked kipper in thick mustard sauce; chopped bacon in thick cheese sauce with chives; scrambled egg with cheese or chutney or smoked fish or diced bacon or mushroom or curry powder; hard-boiled egg with mayonnaise and chopped raw peppers; sausage mashed with meat extract; dressed crab alone or mixed with white sauce or devilled with a little Worcestershire sauce and mace; salmon with chopped cucumber and lemon juice.

All these fillings will make excellent sandwiches, but will be enormously improved if there is also some lettuce or tomato taken with them. These are usually awkward inside the sandwich; it is better to take them separately.

For dessert there can again be quite a choice. Fresh fruit is not only very acceptable but also the simplest. Or you can take some of the sweets described earlier, in a small plastic container. If the main part of the meal is fish, meat, or egg, many people would be glad to finish it with slices of cheese, or cheese and apple, or soft cheese balls with nuts. It is pretty true to say that the success of such meals depends more than anything else on that little amount of extra trouble and imagination. There really is no reason why snack meals should not be as interesting as most hot meals.

APPENDIX

CARBOHYDRATE UNITS

Carbohydrate Units are given for the whole dish unless otherwise stated. The explanation of what Carbohydrate Units are has been given in *This Slimming Business*.

1 Soups (Carbohydrate Units per portion)
- Artichoke, 2
- Bisque of lobster, 2
- Bortsch, 2
- Bouillabaisse, 1; freshwater bouillabaisse, 1
- Cauliflower, 2
- Celery, 1½
- Cherry, 4½
- Chicken broth, 0
- Cock-a-leekie, 1
- Consomme : stock, 0; recipe 1, 0; recipe 2, ½
- Cucumber, ½
- Hare, 1½
- Hollandaise, 1
- Kidney, 1
- Minestrone : without macaroni and haricot beans, ½; with macaroni and haricot beans, 1½
- Mockturtle, 2
- Mulligatawny, 1½; clear, 0
- Mushroom, 0
- Onion, 1½
- Oxtail : clear, 0; thick, 1
- Pot au feu, 0
- Tomato, 1
- Scotch broth, ½
- Shrimp, 1
- Shrimp cheese bisque, 2
- Tomato, 2½
- Vegetable : white 1½; brown, ½
- Watercress, 1
- Stock, 0

2 Fish
- Baked haddock, 4½
- Stuffed plaice: stuffing (both recipes) 4½
- Brandade of cod, 0
- Brill Niçoise, 1
- Devilled lobster, 3
- Fish au vin blanc, 5
- Fish bonne femme, 3
- Fish mayonnaise, 1
- Fish salad with fennel, 0
- Fish salad in aspic, 1
- Lobster Parisienne, ½
- Plaice Dugléré, 4
- Plaice Suchet, 7
- Prawns, curried (including 2 for rice), 9½
- Pickled salmon, 0
- Salmon mousse, 0
- Scalloped fish, 4
- Skate and brown butter, 0
- Sole au gratin, ½
- Sole Rouennaise, 9½
- Baked roes, 1
- Creamed roes, 3½
- Soused mackerel or herring, 0
- Soused (cooked) river trout, 1
- Trout with butter, 0
- Turbot, 2½

Yugoslavian baked fish, 3

3 Meat
  Mixed grill (per portion), 2
  Veal cutlets fried, 0
  Wiener schnitzel, 0
  Boiled fowl : sauce, 6
  Boiled turkey: forcemeat, 4
  Roast meat : stuffing for
    mutton, 5; stuffing for
    pork, 7; stuffing for
    chicken, 9; stuffing for
    turkey, 24½
  Beef olives, 0; forcemeat, 6
  Blanquette of veal, 8
  Braised lamb à la bouquet-
    ière, 8; garnish (per por-
    tion), 3
  Braised pigeon, 5
  Braised liver, 1½;
    forcemeat, 3
  Brawn, 0
  Brown stew, 4½
  Chicken chaudfroid, 9;
    chaudfroid sauce, 6
  Curried meat, 9
  Curry of beef (dry), 0
  Coq au vin, 20
  Duck with orange, 16½
  Galantine of beef, 4½
  Goulash, 4
  Hotpot of bacon, 10
  Hotpot of mutton, 5
  Liver à la française, 0;
    forcemeat 9
  Mince of mutton, 1
  Navarin of lamb, 11½
  Salmi of game, 13
  Savoury ham, 5
  Stewed sweetbreads, 9
  Tête de veau, 1
  Tripe and onions, 4

Tripe, fried, 0
Vienna steaks, 0

4 Cheese
  Cheese and tomato hotpot,
    13
  Cheese soufflé, 9
  Cold cheese soufflé, 0
  Fondue (both recipes), 5
  Lorraine eggs, 0
  Parmesan eggs, 7
  Roes in cheese sauce, 6
  Stuffed marrow, 0
  Stuffed peppers : using
    beans, 5; using peas, 8
  Swiss pie, 0
  Welsh rarebit on
    spinach, ½

5 Savouries
  Angels on horseback, 6
  Aspic moulds (each
    mould), ½
  Cheese and celery bars, 0
  Cream cheese walnuts, 0
  Devilled roes, 0
  Devils on horseback, 9
  Rognons Norges, 1
  Scotch woodcock, 5
  Stuffed mushrooms, 5
  Stuffed prunes, 6

6 Supper Dishes
  Baked eggs : recipe 1, 0;
    recipe 2, 3
  Goodwood herrings, 0
  Herring pie : pastry per
    portion, 4
  Plain omelet, 0
  Scotch eggs : recipe 1, 3;
    recipe 2, 5½
  Spanish eggs, 3
  Spanish omelet (per
    omelet), 1

s.a., 6; sugar, 9

Bavaroise:
s.a., ½; sugar, 4

Caramel custard: caramel,
4; custard: s.a., 1; sugar
2½

Chocolate and ratafia jelly:
s.a., 1, sugar, 2½

Chocolate soufflé, hot:
s.a., 3; sugar, 6

Chocolate soufflé, cold:
s.a., 3½; sugar, 7

Cranberry whip : s.a., 1;
sugar, 3½

Curd pie: s.a., 1½ sugar, 7

Fruit creams with sugar and
custard, 3¼; with sweet-
ener and egg, ½

Orange creams: with sugar
and custard, 2½; with
sweetener and egg, 1

Fruit fool with sugar and
custard, 10; with sweet-
ener and egg, 1½

Fruit salad in melon: s.a.,
3¼; sugar, 4½

Fruit snow s.a., 2; sugar, 8

Honeycomb mould : s.a.,
1½; sugar, 3½

Ice cream, vanilla: s.a., 0
sugar, 2

Junket: s.a., 2; sugar, 4

Lemon snow: s.a., 0; sugar,
5½

Milanaise souffle: s.a., 0,

sugar, 4

Milk jelly: s.a., 1½; sugar,
3

Orange flummery: s.a., 1½
sugar, 5

Orange mousse : with
sugar, 6; without sugar,
1½

Orange soufflé: s.a., 1;
sugar, 4

Orange snow: s.a., 2;
sugar, 5½

Pears baked in cider: with
sugar, 9; without sugar,
4

Prune mousse: s.a., 3;
sugar, 5½

Strawberry mousse: s.a., 1;
sugar, 3½

Swedish apple : s.a., 3½;
sugar, 9

Soufflé omelet: s.a., 0;
sugar, 1

Syllabub: recipe 1: sweet
sherry, no sugar, 4
recipe 2 : sweet sherry,
no sugar, 4; Madiera, no
sugar, 7

Vanilla creams: with sugar
and custard, 3; with
sweetening and egg, 0

Wine jelly :
s.a., 3; sugar, 5½

Zabaglione: s.a., 1;
sugar, 2

INDEX